Tales of Two Canines

Muzzle, nuzzles —

Indy

Koani

Pat

Bruce

Tales of Two Canines

The Adventures of a Wolf and a Dog

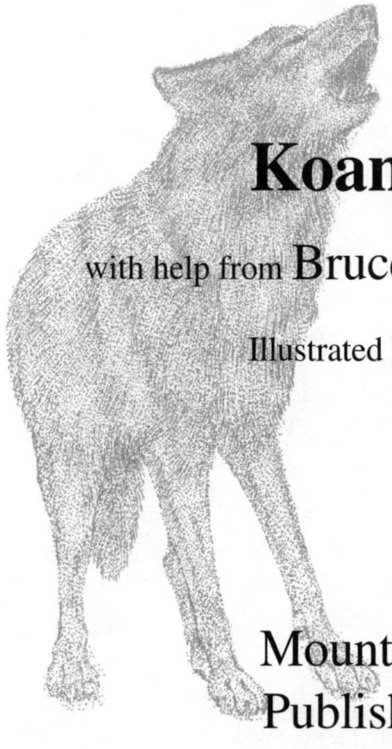

Koani and Indy

with help from Bruce Weide and Pat Tucker

Illustrated by Amber Sidhu

Mountain Press
Publishing Company
Missoula, Montana

1998

© 1998 by Bruce Weide and Pat Tucker

Published in cooperation with Wild Sentry, The Northern Rockies Ambassador Wolf Program. A portion of the proceeds from this book supports Wild Sentry's environmental education programs and provides care for Koani and Indy.

IMAX® is a registered trademark of the Imax Corporation.

Cover and interior design by Bruce Weide

Library of Congress Cataloging-in-Publication Data

Weide, Bruce.
    Tales of two canines : adventures of a wolf and a dog / by Koani and Indy; with help from Bruce Weide and Pat Tucker; illustrator, Amber Sidhu.
       p.   cm.
    Summary: Purports to be letters from the authors' pet dog and wolf, describing their adventures as they travel around the country teaching about wolves.
    ISBN 0-87842-392-3 (alk. paper)
    1. Wolves—Anecdotes—Juvenile literature. 2. Wolves as pets—Juvenile literature. 3. Dogs—Anecdotes—Juvenile literature. [1. Wolves as pets. 2. Wolves. 3. Dogs. 4. Letters.] I. Tucker, Patricia A. II. Sidhu, Amber, ill. III. Title. IV. Title: Tales of 2 canines.
SF459.W63W445 1998
599.773'097—dc21   98-43315
                                                                                   CIP
                                                                                    AC

PRINTED IN THE UNITED STATES OF AMERICA.

This edition published by
MOUNTAIN PRESS PUBLISHING COMPANY
1301 South Third Street West • Missoula, Montana 59806
406-728-1900

To Marcia Dunn
and the crew of KUFM's Pea Green Boat.

"This is a book about dog consciousness. To some people, the subject might seem anthropomorphic simply by definition, since in the past even scientists have been led to believe that only human beings have thoughts or emotions. Of course, nothing could be further from the truth."

–Elizabeth Marshall Thomas, *The Hidden Life of Dogs*

"It is just like man's vanity and impertinence to call an animal dumb because it is dumb to his dull perceptions."

–Mark Twain

"We are told that humans are God's noblest creation. Now who do you suppose found that out?"

–Indy

Contents

Acknowledgments

A BOOK RESULTS FROM the collaborative efforts and cooperation of many people; but before listing the people who dealt with the book during its various stages, there are two large groups of people who need to be thanked. Without them, this book could never have been written. Foremost are all the people who've contributed to Wild Sentry; if not for you folks we could never have taken to the road to present all the programs that led to Koani and Indy's many adventures. Thanks is also due to the listeners of the *Pea Green Boat* who let us know how much they enjoyed the letters from Indy and Koani and went on to demand a book.

Had it not been for Marcia Dunn, host and star of the *Pea Green Boat*, nobody would've ever heard from the canine correspondences. If you're ever driving through western Montana, tune in to *KUFM/KGPR and you might be fortunate enough to hear Marcia read one of Koani or Indy's letters. Her readings are truly inspired.

And speaking of good fortune, we were fortunate to have some good people on the team that put this book together and made it happen. Carol Alette and Susan Hindman went through the manuscript with a fine-toothed comb and pointed out ambiguities and silly mistakes. Amber Sidhu's meticulous and wonderfully rendered illustrations were well worth waiting for. She executed her works of art one dot at a time, each illustration taking her twenty-five to thirty-five hours to complete. Thanks to Genny Cook and her creative flourish with helping Ms. Chloe Dog Cook write her letters

We greatly appreciate the advice, expertise, and encouragement from Mountain Press–to be specific, John Rimel, Kathleen Ort, and Kim Ericsson. Thanks to the Children's Writing Group–Dorothy Patent, Sneed Collar III, Jeanette Ingold, Hannecke Ippish, and Wendy Norgaard–for your advice, patience, and encouragement. And to David Rockwell, who dropped everything to help with the layout and design of the cover, you're truly a friend.

Thank you all from Koani, Indy, Pat, and Bruce.

* By the way, here's where to find KUFM and KGPR on your FM dial:
KUFM: Missoula 89.1, White Sulphur Springs 98.3, Swan Lake 91.1, Butte 99.3
KFPR: Great Falls 89.9, Helena 91.7 & 107.1, Whitefish 91.7, North Missoula 91.5

Who Really
Wrote This Book

LET'S BE CLEAR ABOUT ONE THING: Koani and Indy didn't write this book! Koani is a hundred-pound gray wolf, and Indy is a dog–a Big Sky Snow Roller to be exact. Here's an example of what happened when Indy applied his paws to the keyboard:

"gbHjkmIo9   rTgybHjmdE3wR5dwE3s"

As you can see, a book written by Indy would be difficult to read. And Koani wanted to tear the keyboard to pieces so she could see what was inside. The truth is, Pat and I wrote the book. Oh sure, Koani and Indy provided the stories–they told us what to write, but it's our fingers that actually typed the tales you're about to read.

Who We Are

PAT AND I ARE WOLF WRANGLERS. Pat is also a wildlife biologist, and I'm Bruce, a writer and storyteller. Koani isn't a pet, she's a teacher, an ambassador for her species. Indy is also a teacher and Koani's constant canine companion. The four of us make up the Wild Sentry team. We travel all over the country teaching people about wolves, how they live, what their families are like, and what it is that they really eat. We talk about how stories influence people's imaginations, especially with an animal like the wolf. But that's the subject of another book we wrote, *There's A Wolf In The Classroom!* That book describes how we raised Koani from a pup to feel comfortable in auditoriums, up on stages, and out in front of lots of people. If you're interested you can read it. But I should probably at least tell you how we ended up living with a wolf.

A number of years ago, a filmmaker wanted to make a television program about wolves. Because Pat is a wildlife biologist and a wolf expert, he asked her to help with the film. He had a litter of wolf pups born in captivity so he could film them growing up in a large pen. Right after the pups were born, he asked us if we'd raise one of them to be an ambassador wolf. He wanted to film a scene of a wolf in the classroom. Since Pat and I were already involved with educating people about wolves, we thought that'd be a unique opportunity. The filmmaker said he'd take over caring for Koani when the film was completed. But he didn't. That made Koani our responsibility.

We had two choices: We could either put Koani to sleep or continue doing education programs with her. We couldn't release her into the wild because she never learned how to hunt large animals from her elders (and a wolf can't live on mice alone). We couldn't keep her and live a normal life working a regular job because a wolf requires a lot of care. For example, we take Koani for a "walk" in the morning and again in the evening. Each walk lasts for an hour and a half–that's three hours a day attached to a wolf that wants to run through thorn thickets, dash down hills, and wade across streams. We walk her Christmas morning, Thanksgiving afternoon and Super Bowl Sunday; we head out with her every day in rain, sleet, blazing heat, or snow. What I'm trying to tell you is that living with a wolf is a big responsibility. As for Indy, in the chapter titled "Dog Prison," he explains how he became part of the Wild Sentry team.

Where We Live

THE FOUR OF US LIVE IN WESTERN MONTANA at the edge of a large wilderness called the Selway-Bitterroot. We call our home Gopher Ranch Estate because it's an earth-sheltered house. That means it's dug down into the ground so the dirt insulates the house. Koani has a one-acre enclosure with a grassy meadow, pine trees, a shelter with a bed of straw, an aspen grove, and a little stream with a wading pond. Like most wolves, Koani is very social. Pat, Indy, and I are Koani's

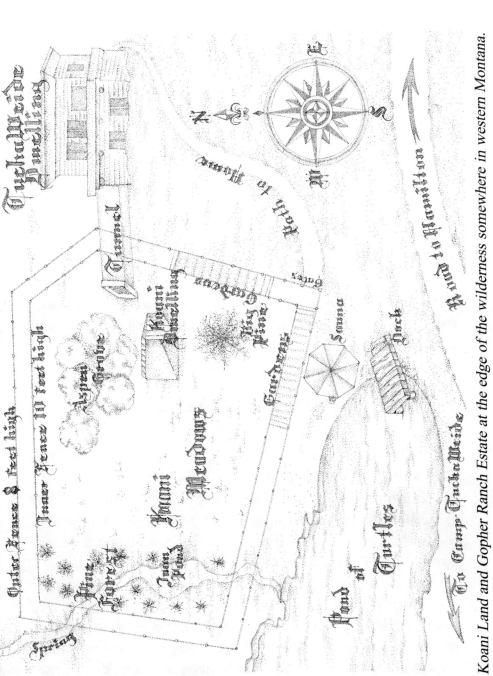

Koani Land and Gopher Ranch Estate at the edge of the wilderness somewhere in western Montana.

pack, and she likes to check up on us from time to time. So, we dug a forty-foot tunnel and it connects her enclosure with a pen in our living room. That way she can come and go as she pleases and we can still have a couch and kitchen. From Gopher Ranch, we've headed out on the many road trips that have taken us to hundreds of classrooms, schools and museums from one end of this country to the other.

Something else we talk to students about is learning to tell the difference between facts, make-believe, and opinions. This book has a bit of all those things in it. For instance, I'm sure you're well aware that Koani and Indy didn't actually speak up and "tell" us these stories. Other animals besides humans communicate, but to understand you have to observe them carefully and listen in a special way, because they talk without using words. Some people think it's wrong to treat animals as if they were capable of experiencing thoughts or emotions; such people say you're being anthropomorphic when you do that. But we know from living with Koani and Indy that they feel happy, sad, lonely, scared, suspicious, or silly. Most children know animals have feelings; it's just that when they grow up, a lot of them forget.

How This Book Came to Be

THESE STORIES WERE WRITTEN FOR CHILDREN. It all started like this. Marcia Dunn hosts *The Pea Green Boat*, the best children's program in the world, broadcast on public radio KUFM in Missoula, Montana. Marcia invited Koani, Indy, Pat, and me to be guests on the program and tell listeners some of Koani's and Indy's adventures. Afterwards, Marcia said, "You're on the road so much, you should send me postcards and I'll read them."

Koani sent a postcard and then Indy. Marcia read them on *The Pea Green Boat*. Later she told us how much people liked the postcards. So Indy and Koani became regular correspondents, and the postcards grew into letters. The years passed by, and the letters stacked up. Marcia said, "You should make a book from all these letters. People would love it."

4

So we did. We read the hundreds of letters that Koani and Indy had written, and we picked out some of the best. Then we talked our friend Amber Sidhu into drawing beautiful illustrations. Amber observed Koani and Indy very closely, went on lots of walks, asked even more questions, and headed back to her drawing table. Carol Alette spent hours and hours carefully proofreading the manuscript and correcting mistakes. The people at Mountain Press said they liked the idea of the book so much that they wanted to publish it.

That's how the letters got written, the illustrations drawn, and the book published. Now there's only one thing left to do. Read it. And that's up to you.

I'm the Star

February 16, 1994

YOU KNOW, IT'S NOT EASY BEING THE SMALLEST one in the group; it means you've got to work harder than the others. Sometimes I hear people say, "Does Indy get jealous of all the attention Koani gets?" I just shake my head and roll my eyes, because I can't believe someone would say that. Where do they get such ideas? It just goes to show you that humans aren't as smart as they think they are. Look, when Koani and I and Pat and Bruce do programs at schools, it's as plain as the muzzle on your face who's the star of the show: ME! I'm not bragging here, it's just fact. After all, lots and lots of people say I'm the cutest dog in the world. Koani is just a plain old wolf.

Believe me, it's tough living with a wolf. For one thing, Koani is twice as big as I am. Most kids ask if we get into fights. Sure, we do sometimes. For instance, not too long ago, Pat put a couple of bones in the enclosure–one for Koani and one for me. It looked to me like Koani got the best bone, so I went to take it from her. She can get cranky about things like that, and she growled at me. I took the bone, and she snapped and snarled and tried to take it back. I had to put her in her place, remind her who's the oldest. I may be the smallest, but I AM the oldest. I snarled and bared my teeth. Bruce says I look like one of those monsters in the *Alien* movies when I act that way. But when Koani and I fight, it's not like we're trying to kill each other–we're just trying to make a point about what belongs to whom

6

and who gets to lie where and important things like that. I bet it's a lot like when you fight with your brothers or sisters–you don't want to hurt them real bad, you just want to let them know you mean business when it comes to matters of great importance, and, of course, you want to win. In this case, Koani backed down, so I won.

A couple of minutes later, I was chewing on that bone when I happened to glance over at Koani, about ten feet away. She appeared awfully interested in something with her nose down in the grass, looking over at me every so often and wagging her tail. I figured that she'd found something even better than the bone I'd taken away from her. Finally, I couldn't stand it any longer; I was wicked curious to see what she'd latched on to. So I trotted over, shoved my nose next to hers, and zammo! She was outta there, and I mean quick–like immediately-right-now. Her jaws clamped around my bone and off she ran. Then she lay down, chewing on it with a self-satisfied smirk on her face like she'd outsmarted me. You could tell she thought she'd really pulled a fast one on me.

But you know what? I didn't really like that bone in the first place. So who cares? But there is a bone I am interested in. Hey, I gotta go. Seee ya!

Love, Indy

Attack of
the Pit Bulls

February 25, 1994

SEND OUT THE WOLF ABUSE PATROL! Somebody rescue me from California! Pat warned us about earthquakes, riots, traffic jams, and drive-by shootings, but I never figured it'd be dangerous to walk through a suburban neighborhood on a balmy winter's day.

Here's what happened: I was plodding along the sidewalk, minding my own business, sniffing all the interesting smells, when suddenly, BAM! Two ferocious pit bulls attacked me. I never even saw them coming. The two savages immediately went for my throat. Fortunately, my fur protected me. Being in strange territory (otherwise, I would've dealt with those two miscreants in short order), I tried to run, but the leash stopped me.

Then things turned kind of wild, crazy, and confusing. A man jumped over the fence to help. A little boy appeared in front of us with a strange grin and said, "It'll be all right!" A short, chubby woman ran up, waving her arms and screaming in Spanish. Indy strutted around and barked about how exciting it all was (little did

8

he know, he'd get all the excitement he could stand in a few days). Eventually, we made our escape.

Three days later, a couple of blocks from where the first attack occurred, an entirely different pair of pit bulls attacked. First, we saw a guy sweeping his driveway. He wore baggy shorts that hung from his hips to below his bony knees, tall white socks (the tops almost met the bottom of his shorts) and a T-shirt with no sleeves. Both of his arms had pictures in the skin. Bruce said, "What a nerdy-looking guy." (It's kind of funny Bruce said that because, as we learned afterwards, that's the warm-weather outfit members of a gang in southern California wear.) And then we spotted the pit bulls. The pit bulls saw us.

Bruce muttered, "Oh no." They launched and ran straight in our direction without making a sound. Indy, who thinks everybody can't help but love him, stepped out front. I backed against a wall.

The first pit bull clamped its jaws on Indy's muzzle and flipped him on his back. The other one slashed at Indy's legs trying to break them. No way was I going to jump into that fight; after all, Indy's the alpha. I looked at Bruce and saw something I've only seen on rare occasions: He turned into a wild animal. He kicked the pit bull fastened to Indy's nose and caught it under the chin. The dog somersaulted backwards.

The gang guy appeared and grabbed the kicked dog by its collar. Spit sprayed out of Bruce's mouth as he screamed at the guy. Bruce looked like he had rabies. Then he crouched in front of the other pit bull and screamed at it. The dog let go of Indy but stood its ground and growled at Bruce. Bruce growled back. As they faced each other off, Indy scrambled away, his nose spurting blood on the sidewalk.

In all the excitement, I guess Bruce hadn't noticed how I'd run around him a couple of times. He stepped back from the pit bull, the two of them still snarling at each other. He said, "Let's go!" I ran, the leash tightened around Bruce's legs, and he crashed on top of Indy, who gave a pitiful cry. They untangled themselves from the leash, and we raced away.

As it turned out, Indy didn't get hurt very badly. His nose swelled, and he got a couple of teensy-weensy puncture wounds on his leg, but he's made a big deal about it and is getting all kinds of sympathy. And me? The way I see it, this is truly the Wild West. I want to go back home where the only things we have to worry about are grizzly bears, mountain lions, and moose.

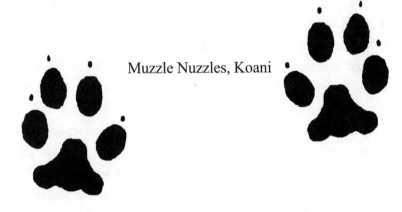

Muzzle Nuzzles, Koani

The Dog
Down The Road

October 5, 1994

WELL, IT'S FINALLY GOTTEN COLD. That's good, because I put on my winter coat a month ago, and I've been too hot ever since! I only change my clothes twice a year. As you know, my clothing is fur. I take off most of it in May, and by September it's nearly all back. Sometimes I'm too hot or too cold, but at least I'm not always wasting valuable time putting clothes on and taking them off like Bruce and Pat do. It drives me crazy waiting while they do that right before a wolf walk.

I've spent this week trying to figure out if there's any way to get rid of Cider, the dog down the road. He just up and moved into my territory, and I don't like it one bit. Every time we walk past the house where he lives, I fluff up my tail and make all the hairs on my back stand straight up; this makes me look REALLY BIG. Then I huff and puff and try to get at him, but the leash always holds me back. Cider skulks around behind the house, peering around the corner, and after we pass he runs out and barks at me. The nerve of that pip-squeak! Bruce and Pat say he's on his own property, but I don't see it that way. I lived in this canyon first and it's MINE. How would you like it if someone moved into your yard and acted like they owned it?

We won't ever be friends, either. As a pup, I used to make new friends all the time. But now that I'm big and grown, I don't want any more pals. I made all the friends I'll ever need back when I was a puppy. Bruce and Pat say that's not a very nice way to be, but

"*I fluff up my tail and make all the hairs on my back stand straight up; this makes me look REALLY BIG.*"

they're humans. I'm a wolf, and that's just the way we are. After all, it makes sense not to let every whimpering dog and wolf into your territory. They'd eat all the deer, and then where would you be? You'd be starving, that's what! So really, I'm pretty smart about all this. I'll figure out how to get him sometime, just you wait.

Muzzle Nuzzles, Koani

Rain, Rain, and More Rain

October 12, 1994

I WISH I WERE FLOATING in the *Pea Green Boat*, on sunny seas, towards enchanted islands where pirates buried treasure chests full of dog biscuits and meaty bones. Instead, I feel like I'm stuck in a submarine. Outside the wolf van, we're surrounded by a dark forest. It's cold and damp, and the rain falls and falls. I'm stretched out on my pad in the van with Bruce and Pat. At least in here it's dry, but it's not very warm. Koani has her thick winter coat on, so she's outside attached to a cable run, and curled up in the portable wolf house that unfolds into a roomy shelter.

We are in Idaho presenting Wild Sentry programs at schools. Yesterday, at Grangeville Elementary School, all the sixth graders got to meet me. From there we drove up through a beautiful canyon colored with autumn yellow, red, and orange to get to Elk City School. The whole school–and that's everybody from first to tenth grade–attended the program. There were too many people!

The kids weren't being mean, and I don't think they intended to act rude, but guess what happens when you pack a whole bunch of excited kids into an echoey gymnasium? You get lots of noise, and that made Koani pretty nervous. To tell you the truth, I got a little nervous myself, and I'm way more used to humans than Koani is.

Today it's Saturday, and we have no programs scheduled because Bruce says there's no school today. Why is that? I'd go to school every day if I could because I love kids. Grownups aren't nearly as

14

much fun. Right now we are just about straight west of our Hamilton home, Gopher Ranch Estate; the only things between home and us are the Bitterroot Mountains and miles and miles of wilderness. See if you can find Grangeville and Elk City, Idaho, on a map. We're in between the two towns on the banks of the South Fork of the Clearwater River–stuck inside the wolf van with cold, wet rain falling. Bruce and Pat lie on their bunk reading books or sit on the ice chest and write in their journal. I'm bored out of my mind. I wish I had some kids to play with or at least a warm fire to lay beside.

Even though there's nowhere I've gotta go, that's all I've got to say. Seee ya!

Love, Indy

The Shredder

October 19, 1994

OH BOY, DO I HAVE A STORY FOR YOU! You know what I did? Well, Bruce and Pat bought a nice new van. It's not really new, but it's a lot newer, roomier, and better looking than the old van. Anyway, I think Indy wrote a letter last week whining about the rain when we went down to Idaho to do some programs. Bruce and Pat were in a school doing the part of the program they do without Indy and me, which must be pretty boring. During that time, they leave us in the van and do something like talk and show pictures.

Waiting in the van is always BORING. Indy gets to lie on the seats or look out the windows, but I have to wait in a cage. Don't ask me why, but I do. They call it a kennel, but the real word is cage. Anyway, while we waited for our curtain call, the latch on the cage door came undone. I pawed at it some more and escaped! Ecstasy! I tore up some upholstery. Then I jumped up onto their bed and sprawled out on Bruce's new sleeping bag. I got to wondering, what's in those sleeping bags that makes them so soft and comfortable? There's only one way to find out, so I ripped a hole in it and pulled out a bunch of stuffing. Big fun! You should have been there.

I'd just started to investigate what was inside the seats and thought maybe afterwards I'd see if I could chew my way out through the door, when I heard the audience howl—that means it's time for us to go onstage. Pat came to get us, and I was so happy to see her. But you should have seen her face when she spotted me in the driver's seat

16

with a big grin on my muzzle. And when she saw the sleeping bag and the upholstery, her jaw about dropped to her knees. I don't know what I did wrong, but it must have been pretty bad. Indy cowered in a corner letting her know he hadn't played a part in any of it. He's such a wimp and tattletale.

Off we trotted to the program. Pat told the audience the whole story. She said that what I'd done provided another example of why wolves don't make good pets. She called me a modern-day velociraptor, whatever that is. You should have seen Bruce's face! It's probably good all those people were there. He couldn't skin me onstage in front of 700 students.

Anyway we're back at Hamilton. In the last two weeks, I showed 3,800 students what a wolf looks like, and Pat and Bruce told all of them the story I just told you, so I must have done a pretty good thing, huh? Unfortunately, I haven't managed to get out of my cage again, but one of these days I'll get another chance to remodel the van.

Muzzle Nuzzles, Koani

Dangers
of the Hunt

October 26, 1994

WE'RE BACK HOME. Pat and Bruce are busy, busy, busy, but Indy and I are on vacation. Actually, Indy thinks programs are fun, so he doesn't see them as work. But I do, and I'm having a good time not doing any programs for a while.

Yesterday we walked along the creek. Hardly any water flows in it now because most of the water gets sucked out for irrigation. Instead of a creek, there's a series of pools that get smaller and smaller as they dry up beneath the summer sun. I spotted trout in one of the little pools and was chasing them around in the water when suddenly I smelled something wonderful. I tugged on the leash and pulled Pat over to where the smell came from. Great! A dead elk calf. A really dead elk calf.

I didn't analyze the situation but got right down to business and started dragging the dead elk calf around. Maggots spilled all over the ground. Of course, I rolled in the rotten meat and wiggling maggots.

How delightful! Meanwhile, Pat played her role as a wildlife biologist and examined the carcass. She looked at its hooves; they were long and curled up.

"That's unusual," she said, "I wonder why that happened?" She looked closer and observed a broken back leg bone sticking out through the skin. "So that's it," she said. "The calf broke its leg and could barely walk. But before it starved to death, its hooves grew long."

I don't know if she's right, but I do know this: if you people allowed a few wolves to run wild and free around here, that elk calf sure wouldn't have starved to death. An animal with a broken leg is exactly the kind of animal we wolves like to find.

I can just hear you say, "Oooh that poor little elk, how could wolves kill and eat a pitiful wounded animal?" Well, if you think about it, you'll probably figure out why we look for animals that have been hurt. Have you ever come face to face with a moose? Even if you haven't, you know they're BIG! Bigger than a horse. Imagine this, okay? Imagine running up and taking a bite out of a full-grown moose. Before wolves get to eat dinner, that's what we have to do—pull down the animal using only our mouths. No hands! Are moose going to just stand there? No way—they're going to kick our brains out if they can. And sometimes moose succeed, and wolves end up dead.

Humans always feel sorry for the "poor" prey animals, but nobody stops to think about us predators. If a moose breaks our jaw, we can't go to a hospital and get it fixed; we wander about growing hungrier and hungrier and weaker and weaker until finally we curl up and die. Those big animals like moose and elk and bison are pretty scary. Even deer can kill wolves when they kick us in the head.

So if you're a wolf and you're hungry, what kind of animal are you going to hunt for? A big, healthy animal or a weak, injured animal like a calf with a broken leg? If you want to keep your brains inside your skull instead of splattered all over the ground, you'll go after feeble animals because they won't kick you in the head or break your jaw. If we can find one that's already dead, so much the better. After all, we're not dumb, you know.

Take right now, for instance: I've got to sign off because Pat's pulling my dinner out of the refrigerator. Now THAT'S a safe place to find a meal!

Muzzle Nuzzles, Koani

The Flashlight Incident

November 2, 1994

Mind you, I know I'm the real star of Wild Sentry, but sometimes I get kind of tired of listening to people carrying on about how neat Koani is. They only say this because she's a wolf and wolves are supposed to be cooool. Oh sure, when she's up onstage in front of a bunch of students, she looks cuddly and innocent as a lamb. But behind the scenes, in real life–oh, the things I could tell you if I wasn't a civilized canine.

Yeah, it's true that Bruce says I lose my mind every once in a while, like when I run off wildly in pursuit of a squirrel or rabbit. But that only happens once or twice or maybe three times a day. That's nothing compared to the things Koani does. A couple of weeks ago, she wrote to you about ripping up the van–she actually bragged about it and had the nerve to call ME a tattletale wimp!

Just between you and me, she's a barbarian! She's got no discipline. For instance, back when Koani was one and a half years old–which in dog or wolf years is like being a teenager–Bruce came into the enclosure to say good night. It was a dark night just after Halloween, and he sat down and petted Koani with one hand. In his other hand, he held a flashlight. After a while, he must've thought Koani was real relaxed so he set the flashlight down. I never would have done that because I know what a wicked sneak she really is.

"Suddenly, Koani's jaws snapped closed on the flashlight. She looked like a wolf-o'-lantern."

Suddenly, Koani's jaws snapped closed on the flashlight and off she dashed. The beam of the flashlight shone inside her big mouth. She looked like a wolf-o'-lantern.

Every time Koani tried to stop and chew on the flashlight, Bruce reached out to take it away from her. She growled at him and ran off with the flashlight again. I think they both knew it was coming to a showdown. At least I was smart enough to know it. Finally, Koani decided she didn't want to run anymore, and she settled in to chew that flashlight into smithereens.

Bruce growled "Nooo" and grabbed the flashlight. Koani's big, sharp teeth clamped onto his wrist. He grabbed her by the ruff and rolled her onto her back, all the while staring fiercely into her eyes and growling. That's how you dominate and discipline a canine–hitting doesn't make sense to us. And so it went, Koani snarling and biting like a beached shark while Bruce held her on her back and growled into her face. It was like something out of caveman times, so totally uncivilized I could barely watch. Finally, Koani looked the other way and went limp, which meant she'd given up. Bruce let her stand and then petted her to reassure her everything was now okay–no grudges. Boy oh boy, do you think they'd cut me that much slack?

Well, it's time to do a program for the kids at Kennedy Elementary in Butte. I guess next week Koani will write you a letter, if she doesn't eat the pen first. Hey, I gotta go. Seee ya!

Love, Indy

Kung Fu
Raccoon
Fighter

December 26, 1994

I WAITED UP ALL LAST NIGHT so I could see Santa, but I must've dozed because there's no doubt that he came here. However, I didn't really get what I wanted. I asked for a reindeer–a whole live reindeer! Instead, I got the frozen head of a deer. And you know what? I don't really think Santa brought it. Pat and Bruce probably got it from the butcher during the hunting season. The reason I don't think Santa brought it is that he doesn't have a freezer on board his sleigh, does he? Does anybody know? But he did stuff my stocking with some other fun treats to eat.

Indy did it again. Have you ever heard him brag about how tough he is and that he's not afraid of cats–not even big ones? Well, last week he once again showed his true colors. Bruce and Pat had gone off and left us at home. Usually, hanging out in the enclosure with Indy is pretty boring, but not that evening because a raccoon invaded our pen!

I saw it first, of course, because whenever Bruce and Pat leave, Indy spends his time moping around by the gate, waiting for them to return, instead of paying attention to his surroundings. (He has absolutely no personal life–he's totally human-oriented.) I chased the raccoon up a spindly tree, and there it clung to a branch about twenty feet above me. Eventually, Indy wandered over, figuring maybe I'd found something to eat. As we all know, Indy doesn't have any common sense; when he found out what it was, he proceeded to hurl himself against the tree over and over, barking and carrying on as if the raccoon would come down if Indy acted ridiculous enough. Maybe Indy thought he could sprout wings. (Who knows if he's capable of thought at all?) Anybody knows that the best thing to do when you've treed something is to lie quietly, out of sight, and wait until it climbs down and into your mouth.

At any rate, the raccoon didn't come down and Indy didn't sprout wings, and that's how things remained until Bruce and Pat returned (a bit late, I might add). Neither of us ran over to greet them when they walked through the gate. But it didn't take long for them to find us, not with Indy barking and whining. Bruce shone the flashlight up into the tree (the same light I ran off with one night). That scared the raccoon, which, in attempting to leap to another tree, fell to the ground!

Indy got to it first. What we heard sounded like a tornado in the brush, what with Indy squalling and squealing, and the raccoon hissing. Being more thoughtful, I hung back. Since Indy's the alpha, I figured it was his responsibility to go the first round with that raccoon. Besides, they wrestled in brush so thick there's nothing any of us could've done to help. Eventually I rushed in, but by then it was too late. The raccoon managed to slip out the fence. Indy roared back, acting like he'd really shown that coon a thing or two. But you know what? I didn't hear the raccoon squeal, holler, or cry, not once. And Indy, he had puncture wounds all over his muzzle.

The next day, his face swelled up big-time. He looked like a boxer who'd been beaten up, punched down, and knocked out. So now, every night he parks himself out by those trees as if the raccoon would be silly enough to come in here again. How dumb can you get? You know, I think Indy really believes he got the best of that raccoon. What can you do with someone as egotistical as that?

Happy Holiday! Maybe Santa will let me have one of his reindeer next year. I wonder which one is fattest? Donner? Blitzen? Dancer?

Muzzle Nuzzles, Koani

Breaking
the Ice

January 2, 1995

I HOPE THAT YOU DIDN'T pay too much attention to Koani's letter
last week when she made fun of me for getting a little bit excited
about the raccoon in our enclosure. You see, it's all in your point
of view–some folks have enthusiasm while others play it cool.
Koani thinks she's hot stuff when she acts cool. You know the
kind; they show no emotion and act like they've seen it all and done
more. But even she can't keep her cool all the time–like when we
pass Cider's house, her tail puffs out and the hair on her back stands
up like she's got a mohawk. (In case you forgot, Cider is the neighbor
dog that Koani would like to assist into the hereafter.)

Me, I believe in enthusiasm, excitement, and unbridled energy. I
can't help it. That's who I am. And that positive, enthusiastic attitude
is what saved me from certain doom down at the animal shelter; but
that's another story. [Editor's note: For the story of how Indy escaped
death by mere minutes, see *Dog Prison* on page 63.] What I'm really
working up to is, maybe I don't have Koani's common sense, but at
least I've got dignity. Here's an example of what I'm talking about.

Both Koani and I love to play on ice. Late in the fall, a skin of
ice formed on our pond. Every day, Koani and I dashed to the shore
and tested the ice to see how strong it felt. Finally, after a couple of
weeks, the ice supported our weight. We had a blast slipping and
sliding, rolling, and playing on the ice.

"The ice broke and she slowly sank into the water–feet, legs, chest, head, and finally all of her."

But, as often happens here in tropical western Montana, a warm front blew in and melted the snow. Now I know Bruce and Pat would call me "a boy of little brains" for admitting this, but to tell you the truth, on the day this happened I wasn't thinking about what warm weather does to ice. I just saw ice on the pond and ran out to play on it. I don't know if it was speed or positive thinking that carried me, but I crossed a good six feet of cardboard-thin ice before it broke. Boy, was I surprised!

I swam to shore, where I shook myself. Bruce, Pat and Koani turned their backs, but I know they were laughing. Bruce whispered something to Pat about me "looking like a drowned rat."

Koani ran to the pond's edge and sniffed at the hole in the ice. She backed away from the cold water, and a grin spread across her black muzzle. Her rear end wiggled about, and she jumped a couple of times as if to say, "What a fine joke on Indy." See, she can't always keep her cool. As for me, personally I don't see any humor in others getting to laugh at my expense.

A couple of hours later, after finishing the walk, Koani ventured out to the end of a small dock that extends over the pond. She leaned forward, placed one paw on the ice, and tested it. The ice held. She leaned farther forward and, with delicate ease, placed her other paw on the ice. The ice buckled and cracked. She scrambled backwards furiously, but her center of gravity hung too far out from the dock. The ice broke and she slowly sank into the water–feet, legs, chest, head, and finally all of her. Koani swam for shore, her nose plowing through the ice like the bow of a black icebreaker. She dashed onshore, shook the water from her coat, and stretched forward with her head low, rear end up, and tail out–the entire rear-unit wiggling about rapidly. This behavior, mildly translated, means "great!" or "too much!" She jumped up to lick Bruce's face, soaked him but good (which I thought was wicked funny), and then dashed around in wide circles.

Koani likes jokes. It doesn't matter whether she's the joker or the one the joke is played on; what's important is that there be jokes. To her, it's just as funny to be the clown in a slapstick ice antic as it is to nibble-pinch Bruce or Pat on the rear during a program. As for me, I've got an image to maintain. I've got dignity.

One last thing: Someone asked if Koani or I ever try to catch fish and eat them. I don't. Fish are slimy and wet and cold, and you have to go in the water to get one. I don't want anything to do with fish or swimming. Koani isn't especially interested in fish, however I remember once when she waded out in Red Fish Lake and found a dead trout floating belly up. She played with that fish for half an hour, tossing it in the air, trying to make it sink, and finally carrying it onshore where she rolled on it, which I thought was pretty uncivilized. But then she's a wolf, so what can you expect?

What's that? I smell something good to eat. Hey, I gotta go. Seee ya!

Love, Indy

Ms. Chloe Dog Cook Introduces Herself

January 9, 1995

H<small>I, MY NAME IS</small> M<small>S</small>. C<small>HLOE</small> D<small>OG</small> C<small>OOK</small>. Indy and Koani said I could write this letter because I'm their best friend and I'm visiting them this week. I listen to the *Pea Green Boat* all the time to hear news from Indy and Koani, because I don't get to see them much anymore. I used to see them every day when they lived in Missoula, but now they live at Gopher Ranch Estate, which is a long car ride from Missoula. I don't blame them for moving though; Gopher Ranch is a great place. There are lots of fun things to do like chew on deer heads and tear elk hides apart and slide on the pond ice and go for walks and chase squirrels.

I guess I should tell you who I am. Besides being responsible, trustworthy, and loyal, I'm what's called a Harlequin Great Dane, so I'm BIG. I'm spotted black and white–that's where the Harlequin part comes from. Lots of people think I'm a Dalmatian, and that offends me because Great Danes are much more respectable than Dalmatians. In the old days, Dalmatians merely ran beside coaches and looked pretty. But do you know what noble deeds Great Danes performed? We lived in castles and hunted bears with kings! Now I just hunt squirrels, but they're kind of like bears. After all, they climb trees.

I've known Indy and Koani since they were little. I'm a year older than they are, so I'm more mature. In the old days, they always used to pick me up for their afternoon walk. I wanted to be ready, so every day I sat peering out the upstairs window watching for them to come into view. Since they moved away, I've quit doing that. Now, about once a month, Bruce or Pat stop by and give me a ride up to Gopher Ranch. This time, I'm here for a week, and we're having a great time wrestling and chewing on bones and chasing squirrels, of course. Koani won't admit it, but I'm faster than she is. The only thing that keeps me from catching her when we play tag in the pen is that she knows all the shortcuts.

Pat says the reason Koani likes me so much is that I'm a good muzzle nuzzler, and I am too. We nuzzle, nuzzle, and nuzzle, which means we lick each other all over the face. Indy isn't very good at it; he always turns his head away—kind of like humans. I've got another great skill, too. I manufacture Chloe mousse in my mouth! After we've played and wrestled and pinned each other and I've managed to lick Indy from head to toe and he's all wet from my thick saliva, his fur sticks out in spikes. He looks really cool. Bruce and Pat say it's yucky, but what do they know? They're old, and besides that, they're humans. Just to prove how silly they are, they think it's gross when Koani and I eat horse poop! Can you imagine thinking that's gross? We especially like it when it's frozen. Then we call it poop-sickles!

I've got to go, but before I do, Koani wants to tell you something. She says to tell you that next week, Indy will probably write about how he's a hero and would have managed to provide the whole pack with a year's worth of meat if only Koani and Bruce hadn't been so inept. She says that when it's her turn to write again, she'll tell you what really happened.

   Gobbers of Slobbers,
                        Ms. Chloe Dog Cook

Moose Attack

January 17, 1995

INDY ALMOST GOT US KILLED! That's how Bruce tells it. I admit it was a wildlife encounter of the wildest kind–but the way I see it, I led us into a wicked grand adventure. After all, when you're named after Indiana Jones, you can't sit around like a couch potato, can you? Here's what happened:

Bruce checked the thermometer as we began our evening walk. "Twelve degrees," he said, and drew the parka hood over his head. We started up the creek, walking on the ice, which is kind of fun in a suspenseful way–the same way that a scary movie is fun. Sometimes the ice cracks or buckles or shifts. You never know if it might break and dump you in the creek. Ever since that day the ice on our pond busted out beneath me, I've learned a lot about ice. It doesn't scare ME, but Koani can be such a scaredy-wolf at times.

So we crossed to the other side of the creek and thrashed our way through thick brush. Koani stopped. She sniffed the air and then sniffed all around a short aspen tree. Her ears perked up, her eyes opened wide, and she got into her hyperalert mode. She was on to something. Then I smelled it and got excited too.

We started moving again, Koani with her nose to the ground. I pushed into the lead to be point man. "Indy, get back here," said Bruce. "There might be a mountain lion out there." That'd be too cool, I thought, and dashed farther ahead. The smell of whatever it was–I'd never smelled anything like it–grew stronger and stronger. I had my nose to the ground following the scent, when I happened to look up, which was a good thing because I almost ran into a hairy tree. Another hairy tree grew right beside it and two more behind.

I heard a snort above my head and looked up, right into the beady eyes of a huge, hairy beast. I barked and bayed, but instead of scurrying up a tree like raccoons do or running away like deer do, this huge, hairy beast pawed the ground with monstrous Clydesdale-sized hooves and tried to stomp me into the ground! He swung his head, which was about the size of Koani, and tried to ram me. I ran in and around and through his long, gangly legs and then hightailed it out of there to find Bruce and Koani. I wanted to share the wonderful adventure. I was also being practical. After all, if we could bring this guy down, we'd have enough meat for a long time. And, I'll admit that I felt a little bit intimidated by that huge, hairy beast. Now this next part is how Bruce tells the story. He says:

Indy started baying like a hound of the Baskervilles. I figured he had a raccoon up a tree. Koani keyed into Indy's barking, leaped into the air, and rocketed towards the racket. I ran as fast as I could, trying to keep up, being dragged behind a one-hundred pound wolf gone ballistic as the brush whipped my face so I could hardly see.

Suddenly, I noticed this tan blur, which I knew was Indy; he dashed between my legs. I looked up and saw Koani running back towards me. I had just enough time to think, 'I've got a bad feeling about this,' when I saw an immense, dark, shaggy moose with enraged eyes charging us.

His head swept back and forth, and his hooves lashed out from side to side. That moose was like a runaway locomotive, and I stood right on the track unable to move. I wanted to dive out of the way, but I couldn't because I was tangled in the leash and Koani was pulling in the opposite direction from where I wanted to go. That and the

"I heard a snort above my head and looked up, right into the beady eyes of a huge, hairy beast."

thick brush made it impossible to move. Finally, I leaned over and fell to the side. The moose roared by, brushing against me as he passed. I smelled his musty odor as I hit the ground. I turned my head to see where the moose stood, expecting at any moment to feel his hooves stomp me into mush. But when I turned my head, I saw only the inside of my hood.

Now I'll take over the story again. What Bruce doesn't realize is that I saved his life. Being back with my mates filled me with a new sense of confidence. I ran up to the moose barking and baying, which drew his attention away from Bruce. Koani got into the spirit of things and lunged at the moose as he tried to pummel us with his hooves.

Bruce struggled to his feet just as the moose charged me. I ran behind Bruce, who tried to climb an alder tree. Unfortunately, the tree broke to pieces; I guess it was rotten. Fortunately, the moose stopped five feet from Bruce. They stared at each other. Koani lunged at the moose again, and it turned to stomp her, but she ran behind a tree, further tangling the leash.

For a while everyone stood still staring at each other. Figuring that things needed to be stirred up, I charged the moose again, barking up a storm. Bruce screamed words at me that I can't repeat. The moose lowered his head, white clouds of steam jetting from those huge nostrils, and charged. I pulled a one-eighty spin-around and ran behind Bruce. He waved his arms wildly and hollered, and the moose stopped five feet away.

To shorten an already long story, everyone weenied out on me. After three attacks, which in my opinion were pretty mild, I could tell Koani didn't want to tangle with the moose anymore. As for Bruce, well, I didn't have to be a rocket scientist to realize that he was scared of that moose from the start. Even the moose didn't have his heart in this grand adventure; he was just a grumpy bull who wanted to be left alone so he could conserve energy because it was so cold. I was the only one there willing to have fun!

Anyway, Bruce finally reeled Koani in. He yelled at me enough that I eventually stopped charging the moose, which stood his ground staring at us with those beady, mad eyes while he snorted jets of steam that looked like twin geysers. Even though the leash tangled in the brush a couple of more times as we backed away through the thicket, by and by we put enough distance between us and the moose that everyone began to relax.

So you can see why I think Bruce is being a bit dramatic when he says that I almost got us killed. The way I see it, Bruce and Koani just didn't know a good time when it stared them in the face! I get exasperated just thinking about it. Hey, I gotta go. Seee ya!

Love, Indy

The Truth about Moose

January 24, 1995

YOU WON'T BELIEVE WHAT'S HAPPENED! We're in Albuquerque. That's in New Mexico–a long ways from Montana. It's desert around here and not a good place for a wolf like me to live, mostly because there's cactus everywhere. Try taking a hike barefoot through cactus country and you'll know what I mean. If you walk slowly and watch where you're going, you can spot the cactus, even the little ones. But when you're hot on the trail of a jackrabbit, who's got time to look for cactus?

And that's what happened to Indy this morning. He shot off after a rabbit and returned to the van limping. Pat rolled him on his back and pulled out the thorn; that horrible thing was an inch long! ECK! I can't believe Indy lets them do that with him. When I get a thorn in my paw, I won't even let them look at it. If they so much as try to touch my foot, I snarl and snap. When you're a wolf, you can't be too careful because you never know what a human might try to do.

Tomorrow we present a program at the University of New Mexico. The university's mascot is the lobo, and that's Spanish for me: WOLF. It's kind of funny because there haven't been wolves around here for fifty years. People are weird. They move into a meadow where elk found food during the winter, tear it up, build houses and name the road Elk Lane, even though the elk won't ever return. I can't figure it out, and mostly I don't even try.

And while I'm on the subject of weirdness, I thought Indy conjured up a pretty amazing version of what happened when that moose charged us. What a bragger, saying that he saved Bruce from the moose. That moose scared Indy to death. Whenever it looked at him, he hightailed it between Bruce's legs. Being connected to Bruce by that stupid long leash, I couldn't do much of anything. If Indy really wanted to provide our pack with meat, he should have grabbed hold of that moose by the nose while Bruce and I attacked him from the sides. Every wolf knows that's how you kill a moose. Indy just made him mad and nearly got us all trampled.

I hope you guys don't believe everything you hear. Indy likes to tell stories in such a way that he ends up looking like the hero. It seems to me that people tend to do that, too. What do you think?

Muzzle Nuzzles, Koani

The Oldest Town
in America

January 31, 1995

W E'RE IN THE DESERT down in New Mexico. There are horrible thorns called "goat heads" all over the ground. These thorns, which are actually small balls with lots of spiky thorns protruding out, are constantly getting stuck in the pads of our paws–I'm talking about Koani and me, since Bruce and Pat wear shoes. Koani can't figure out why I submit to allowing Pat or Bruce pull the thorns out. If she didn't act so independent, wild, and suspicious, the answer would come to her easily. I let them do it because the thorns hurt. Pat and Bruce have thumbs and fingers that allow them to pluck thorns from my paws–one of the few advantages of being human. Of course, the reason humans have hands is that back when the world was being made, the Great Creator saw that the supreme creation–dogs–liked being petted and sometimes needed thorns, burrs, and ticks plucked.

So far, things have been pretty calm for a hero like me. We did a program in Albuquerque and Socorro. Everybody loved me. They thought I was great. But that's nothing new. After all, I am the star of the show. We drove out to the Acoma Pueblo; it's a village where Native Americans settled 900 years ago, and that makes it the oldest continuously lived-in town in America. However, to tell you the truth, I got wicked bored because while Bruce and Pat toured Acoma, Koani and I stayed in the van. I understand why they left Koani behind, but it didn't make any sense to leave me. I'm sure the Acoma people wanted to meet me.

Bruce told me some of the stuff he learned on the tour. Back in the 1600s, Spanish priests lived with the Acomas. Things went okay at first, but then the Acomas got tired of the priests telling them what to do all the time. So they tossed the priests out of the village. Unfortunately for the priests, the Acoma village is perched on top of a flat-topped mesa surrounded by cliffs 400 feet high.

The Acomas originally settled up on the sandstone mesa to get away from people who caused problems. There's still no running water or electricity in the village. They get their water from cracks in the sandstone that are 35 feet deep.

After Pat and Bruce finally returned, we all went on a walk along the bottom of Enchanted Mesa. I figured it was called that because there were rabbits on the top. But Bruce told me it got the name because long ago Acomas lived on top of that mesa too. Steps and handholds carved into the rock allowed them to go up and down. One stormy day, a bolt of lightning destroyed the steps and handholds, trapping those who remained on top. Some of the people on top wanted to be with their relatives so badly that they flung themselves from the cliff tops to the rocks below. The rest of the Acoma people trapped on the mesa starved to death.

Even without steps or handholds–which, having no hands, I don't use–I could've reached the top to chase rabbits. But Bruce wouldn't let me. He said the Acomas don't allow people up there. Technically speaking, I should be allowed on top because I'm not a person. See, there's another advantage of being a dog: most rules are made for people. Given the choice, wouldn't you rather be a dog?

Tonight, we're doing a program in a New Mexican town called Truth or Consequences. Hey, I gotta go. Seee ya!

Love, Indy

The Woman Who Wanted Eagles to be Nice Birds

February 6, 1995

W E'RE CAMPED AT A PLACE called City of the Rocks near Silver City, New Mexico. Big piles of huge rocks rise up out of the desert sand; between the boulders, we've found neat passageways, and on top there are great views. Indy refuses to climb the rocks because he's scared of heights. He's such a weenie dog. I love exploring routes to the top because the higher you get, the more you can see.

We did a lot of school programs in New Mexico this week, including programs in Silver City. A couple of years ago, someone else came to the school to talk about wolves, and a bunch of women–they called themselves Cow Belles–barricaded the school doorway. Can you believe that? But no one blocked me from entering the school. Thursday night, we presented an evening program in Silver City and 420 people came to see me. Our friends worried that someone might try to kill me because lots of people around here hate wolves. But no one dared. Of course, Indy thinks no one messed with us because they're scared of him. He's so silly, but he's cute.

We stopped at a bird refuge called Bosque del Apache. Bruce and Pat wanted to watch a bunch of big white birds–they called them snow geese–and we're not talking about a goose or two. We watched from the banks of a shallow lake. Just before sunset, thousands of geese flew towards us and landed in the water. Bruce said he'd heard there were more than 11,000 of them.

43

The next morning, we returned to the lake before the sun rose. As the sun cleared the horizon, the air filled with the noise of honking and the sound of thousands of geese taking flight. Their wings beat furiously and created a loud swooshing roar as the birds fought gravity and rose into the sky. Personally, I thought there were too many of those geese and there needed to be a few wolves around.

After the geese flew away to spend the day feeding in nearby cornfields, Pat spotted an eagle resting in an old dead tree. The eagle spread its wings and swooped down with talons outstretched and attacked a snow goose that stood on the ice. Every time the eagle slashed the goose, a cloud of white features fluttered through the air and settled on the ice. The eagle dove for another attack and the goose batted the eagle with its wing. The eagle looked as if it was seeing stars because, believe me, a goose's wing is definitely a weapon. Now, I don't have too many good things to say about eagles, because for the most part, they just steal meat from hard-working predators like me. But what happened next was so totally ridiculous that I have to defend the eagle, even if it is a messy old scavenger.

An older woman walked by complaining about one thing and another. Pat, who seems to think it's her duty to help people have a good time, told the woman, "There's a drama in real life going on out on the ice." Pat pointed out the eagle and goose and handed the woman a set of long black tubes–I think she called them binoculars. The woman watched for a while and then slowly lowered the binoculars.

"Someone should put a stop to that!" she announced with outrage. "Someone should help that poor snow goose." I couldn't believe my ears. Certainly, I would like to have stopped the eagle and helped that goose right into my stomach. But I don't think that's what the woman had in mind.

Pat explained to the woman, "I know how you feel. But the eagle could very well starve to death if it doesn't kill the goose, and then we'd feel sorry for the eagle."

The woman shook her head self-righteously. "Well, why can't the eagle just fly up to the fields and eat corn with all the nice birds?"

It was such a silly statement, I laughed out loud. However, no one knew it because no one understands my laugh. An eagle's beak isn't shaped for shoveling up corn like the flat, rounded bill of a goose or duck. The beak of an eagle is hooked and sharp; it's shaped for tearing off hunks of meat–mostly, as I've said, meat they steal from honest, hard-working predators like wolves. Even if an eagle wanted to eat corn, it could only eat one kernel at a time–the poor critter would run out of energy and starve just trying to feed itself.

Humans can be pretty ignorant, which always leaves me wondering: how come there are so many of you around? You'd think any animal that dumb would be extinct by now.

Muzzle Nuzzles, Koani

"I gave myself a new hairdo."

High Fashion:
The Stegosaurus Look

February 21, 1995

WE'RE IN SOUTHERN CALIFORNIA, and I'm sleeping under a palm tree! Whoever heard of wolves and palm trees going together? But here I am. To celebrate being in California and to show all these cooool people that Montanans aren't ignorant about high fashion, I gave myself a new hairdo. Not only does my hair look smashing, but it also smells great. I bet you'd think so, too. You must like the stuff I used for my hairdo because you smear it all over your houses, cars and fences.

It happened like this. Bruce and I headed out for a walk. Suddenly I smelled this delectable smell and rushed out to the end of my leash to find a little pool of gray, sticky, smelly stuff. Well, then I did the only sensible thing: I rolled in it.

It was heavenly!

By the time Bruce pulled me away, I'd managed to spread it all around my neck, on my ears, and down my back. Now, I have to admit that, in the beginning, I was only interested in the smell. I didn't think about the visual effect; after all, a style-conscious wolf is much more interested in smell than appearance. But the visuals

47

turned out great. The stuff was paint–gray paint. Bruce and Pat keep calling it oil-based, whatever that means.

So there we were in the middle of the desert, with nothing to remove the paint and a hot sun baking it to a fine crusty finish. You should see me now. Everyone just raves about it. I have gray spikes sticking out all around my neck and down my back. I look sort of like a stegosaurus. Just wait until those Los Angeles pit bulls that attacked me last year get a load of this. They'll know they aren't dealing with no hick from Montana.

I don't know why you waste this oil-based stuff on houses when you could roll in it and look as good as me. People are so weird. In fact, I'm getting kind of mad because Pat and Bruce keep cutting off pieces of my spiky hair. Do your parents ever brush your hair after you've worked a long time to make it look just right? Well then, you understand how I feel. I know what I like, and I don't need their help. After all, I'm a big wolf now.

Next, we head for San Diego, and from there we'll do programs all the way up the California coast. Don't be surprised if you start seeing all the models in fashion magazines with paint-spiked hair. My only regret is that I didn't roll in a puddle of day-glow pink. Wouldn't that have been cooool?

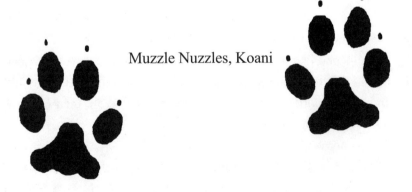

Muzzle Nuzzles, Koani

Killer Cactus, Natural Wonders, and the Philosophy of Rabbit Chasing

February 25, 1995

We're in San Diego, California, now. The ocean, beaches, waves, and surfers are okay, but I miss the desert. Rabbits ran all over the desert, and I haven't seen even ONE hopping along the beach. There are beach bunnies here, but they don't look anything like rabbits. Nothing beats chasing rabbits; it's the finest sport in the whole wide world. In fact, calling it a sport is degrading. Rabbit chasing is a way of life. It's a reason for living. I'm sure you agree with me, so I'll give you some inside information. I'm going to tell you about the best rabbit-chasing places in the great Southwestern desert.

Cochise's Stronghold in the Dragoon Mountains of Arizona–with oaks, manzanita, and sycamores–provides excellent rabbit encounters. I'm pleased to report that the rabbits there are healthy, fast and quite worthy of a hearty chase.

I rate Saguaro National Monument as the worst place. Actually, chasing rabbits there could be great, except Pat and Bruce kept me tied on the leash. Boy, it's frustrating to spot a rabbit and bolt into action only to find yourself bungied backward by a stupid leash. I understand why they keep Koani on a leash; she's a wolf for heaven's sake. But I'm a dog and a cute, civilized dog at that.

To tell you the truth, national parks and national monuments aren't very interesting to me because there are always rules that say domestic animals are supposed to be on a leash. Rangers say the rule was made to preserve natural wonders. But here's what I naturally wonder about that stupid rule–the rabbits never get chased so they become slow, unhealthy and fat, and what's so naturally wonderful about that? Here's something else that leaves me wondering: people are domestic animals, too, but they're not on a leash. If you want to preserve national parks and monuments, people should definitely be on leashes. Here's a story that shows you what I'm talking about.

Saguaro National Monument is named after the saguaro cactus, which is the cactus of cactuses–actually I should say cacti. Anyway, when someone says the word "cactus," a saguaro is the cactus that probably appears in your imagination. It looks like a tall, fat pole with thick arms that branch out and grow straight up parallel to the main body. Saguaros have to be fifty-five years old before they can flower, fruit and produce the seeds needed to make baby saguaro cacti. They're sixty years old before those arms begin to branch out. Anyway, that's what Bruce claims he learned; now back to the story.

There was this guy with a gun–a human, of course, because they're the only animals that carry weapons–and he decided he wanted to shoot a saguaro. Shooting a cactus makes about as much sense to me as shooting the ground (how could you miss?) and much less sense than chasing a rock. So he walked up to a tall saguaro and shot it. That excited him, so he shot it again. Shooting the cactus must've entertained him BIG TIME because he kept pumping lead into that thorny vegetable. I guess he wanted to see if he could chop down a saguaro with bullets. He succeeded. The sixteen-foot-tall saguaro, which weighed more than two thousand pounds, crashed to the ground. It landed right on top of the guy and killed him deader than a doornail. Now, if he'd been on a leash that never would have happened, and both he and the saguaro would be alive today.

"Rabbit chasing is a way of life. It's a reason for living."

Back to my favorite subject, chasing rabbits. The very best place was where we stayed along the Colorado River, which forms the border between Arizona and California. The rabbits out there are pretty fit. At least, I never managed to get one. Sometimes I get asked, "Why chase rabbits if you never catch them?" This is another example of how naturally silly people can be. In this case, they're wondering, "Why do something unless you get something in return?" Koani is that way too; as soon as she sees that she can't catch a squirrel or a rabbit or a ruffed grouse, she quits. You guys are all worried about getting something for your efforts, attaining a goal, and winning a reward. To me, the pursuit is the reward. The chase is what makes me happy.

By the next time I write to you, we'll be in La Habra, California; that's where pit bulls attacked Koani and me last year–but that's a whole other story. I sure hope it doesn't happen again this year. Raccoons, mountain lions and moose don't scare me, but I sure don't like pit bulls. Writing about chasing rabbits makes me hungry. I gotta go. Seee ya!

Love, Indy

Showdown
in Silver City

March 17, 1995

IT'S NO WONDER people think the country is in bad shape: nobody
ever agrees with anybody else, and nothing good ever happens.
People believe those things because that's all they ever hear on the
TV or read in newspapers. And, as I just learned, most reporters
think there's a "story" only if someone gets shot, beat up or killed,
but not if something good happens.

An example of what I'm talking about happened a month ago at
our program in Silver City, New Mexico. Silver City is a small town
located where a lot of people raise cattle and graze them on public
land or dig silver and other materials out of the ground. A bunch of
these people get hot and bothered about wolves. I'm not talking
about hands-on-your-hips, eye-rolling kind of upset; I'm talking
about red-faced, eyes-bulging-out, foaming-at-the-mouth MAD.

I think Koani already told you this, but a few years ago, a school
in Silver City tried to have a wolf education program, and a group
of women ranchers stopped it. They called themselves the Cow Belles
(kind of a cute name, isn't it?), and they formed a barricade to block
the wolf from entering the school. When I hear about things like that,
I always think of something Snoopy once said: "I love people–it's the
human race I can't stand."

So anyway, here we were headed to do a program in a town
where most of the human race feels pretty hostile towards wolves.

To be completely honest, we all felt a bit worried. Bruce joked about buying us bulletproof body armor, but I could tell that deep inside, he didn't think it was a laughing matter. We weren't the only ones thinking violence might occur. A bunch of newspaper reporters and television news teams arrived in Silver City to attend our program. That evening, the auditorium filled beyond capacity with 450 people. Some stood in back and some sat in the aisles. New Mexico Fish and Game sent a special officer, and security guards stood at the entrances. The air felt electric; everyone was tense and edgy. You'd have thought we were headed for a showdown at the OK Corral.

And there was the CNN news team to cover the story, a videographer, a sound person, and a pretty-boy reporter. Bright lights flooded the stage. The videographer poked his camera right in Pat's face as she spoke, and the soundman held a microphone on a pole just above her head. Bruce and Pat did their part of the program, and then Koani and I bounded onstage. I wasn't concerned about anyone trying to shoot me. After all, who could possibly want to harm a dog as wicked cute as me? But I worried that if someone tried to shoot Koani, they might miss and hit me.

At the end of the program, one guy wearing a cowboy hat was pretty dedicated to the notion that wolves kill humans. I know from personal experience that a certain wolf, whose name starts with K, can be dangerous to some dogs. But, like Pat and Bruce explained to the cowboy and the rest of the audience, "There haven't been any documented cases of healthy wild wolves killing humans in North America. This doesn't mean that wolves absolutely never have or never will kill a human, but it's not something to worry about. You're in far more danger driving to the grocery store than you'd ever be walking in the woods where wolves lived."

The audience stood up and applauded. I think most of these people were the regular folks of Silver City—not ranchers or environmentalists—and I believe they were tired of hearing the anti-wolf crowd telling lies and exaggerating and carrying on blah, blah, blah about how horribly awful wolves are, and the pro-wolf

*Koani explores City of Rocks, New Mexico, just before the showdown
in Silver City.*

people making the wolf out to be a saint. Anyone who lives with Koani knows she isn't a saint.

After the program, people complimented us and said they appreciated Pat and Bruce talking to them honestly and stating the facts without resorting to exaggeration. People said they wished they got the straight story more often, because then people could make decisions and compromises and work towards solutions instead of arguing and shouting at each other. So the way I see it, our program concluded with a happy ending instead of a fight.

And that's exactly why we didn't make the news. The CNN pretty-boy reporter said, "Nothing happened." The Albuquerque newspaper journalist said, "There's no story."

I wanted to bite them both. After all, that's exactly what they wanted–some violence. Any fool can write a story about violence. But we found ourselves in a situation where things easily could've turned hostile but didn't. Of course, that's because I came out and calmed people down, and they learned stuff and agreed on things; now THERE'S a story worthy of a Pulitzer Prize, especially when it takes place in a town like Silver City. It takes a skilled writer like me to report a story like that. Now I'm hungry. I gotta go. Seee ya!

 Love, Indy

Born to Be Wild

March 29, 1995

I WAS A BIG SPLASH at the Monterey Bay Aquarium. Both programs sold out a week in advance. On the day of the big event, the theater filled with people, and they all wanted to see me. Tonight we present another big show in San Francisco. Now I know how Madonna must feel. Oh sure, people also come to programs expecting to see Koani and maybe even Bruce and Pat. But that's okay, I'm not an attention hog. In fact, I feel kind of sorry for them; it must be hard on their self-esteem when everyone pays more attention to me than to them. But hey, we can't all be big fish in a little pond.

The truly big event came the day after the aquarium program. That's when two hundred dudes on Harley motorcycles roared into Holly Farm, the place where we stayed in Carmel Valley. They came to see me. And Koani too, I guess. Anyway, these guys were bearded and burly, full-on motorcycle dudes wearing black leather pants and jackets studded with silver spikes. They wore vests with skulls on the back. They strutted around in big ol' black leather boots. Knives and chains hung from their belts. They rode really trick motorcycles–I mean bikes, man–with shiny chrome exhaust pipes, beautiful metallic gas tanks, and high-reach handle bars; and one guy had a snarling wolf painted on his tank.

As soon as Koani heard the choppers motoring into the parking area above us, she started stressing. We had a nice, sandy courtyard all to ourselves, and it was surrounded by an adobe wall and flowers.

The forever-falling rains had finally stopped, so we could stretch out in sunny or shady places to catch a few *z*'s. But when Koani heard the band start playing below our courtyard and people walking past, she wigged out Big Time. She paced back and forth and crushed tulip blossoms in her jaws. She bit Bruce and started a fight with me. Of course, I won, though Bruce might've had a little to do with that. Her cable line was attached to two stakes that were as big around as your arm. She snapped one of them into three pieces and jumped up onto the adobe wall to see what was going on. Being the sensitive dog that I am, I could tell that she felt uneasy.

Maybe she was wicked nervous about all those motorcycle dudes, because you know how you hear stories and see movies where the bikers are wild, bad, and mean. But Koani should know better; those are the same kind of stories that people tell about wolves. I know that the bikers are pretty nice because I slipped out and mingled with the crowd. They fed me chunks of burgers, let me lick the chili off their plates, petted me, and called me the cutest dog in the world.

As the roar of their choppers faded away and they rode off into the sunset, I felt sad to see them go. Koani finally started relaxing. What a silly wolf girl. Well, that's it for now, and remember, don't play in the street; it can leave you feeling run down. Hey, I gotta go. Seee ya!

Love, Indy

58

Good News and Sad News

April 17, 1995

WE'RE HOME! It's great to be back in Montana. It's so much nicer than everywhere else we've been. Koani and I have been roaring around making sure everyone in the neighborhood knows we're back. We do that by urinating on bushes and tree trunks and whatever else is handy. Then we scratch deep furrows of dirt. Koani has scent glands between her toes, so when she scratches she leaves an odor in the dirt. I don't have them because I'm a dog, but I scratch anyway. I do a lot of things wolves do, even though it doesn't make sense for dogs to do them anymore. Pat says it's because of instincts. I say I do it because it feels good.

We did find one sad thing here at home. There's been a coyote couple living nearby. We see them quite often out in the fields hunting mice and bunnies. I always dash over and try to introduce myself, but they run away. I guess they're shy. Still, we like them. Sometimes, we yell back and forth at each other during the night; that's fun.

Anyway, on one of our walks I smelled something funny and ran over to investigate. It was one of the coyotes. He didn't run away this time because he'd been shot! We all felt sad. He was right near their den. I hope his wife isn't going to have puppies. Pat says humans shoot coyotes just because they're coyotes. People blame coyotes for killing lambs and stuff. Well, maybe some coyotes do that, but this one sure didn't. We don't even have any sheep around here. He was just doing what he should do, which was bunny hunting.

Speaking of bunnies, I hunted for the Easter bunny all day Sunday. I thought for sure I'd finally catch one. But I didn't see or even smell anything that resembled bunny. Darn. Maybe next year.

One other thing I thought you'd be interested in: when I walked onstage in San Francisco, the audience gave me an ovation! Now I really know I'm the star. Koani's so jealous. But I tell her she needs to work harder. So at the next program, guess what she did? She grabbed a piece of pizza that was backstage, carried it out in front of everyone, and rolled in it! A perfectly good piece of pepperoni pizza and she smushed it into her fur. I was wicked shocked. As soon as I could, I rushed over and saved it. Then I did what any self-respecting dog would do. I ate it. I just can't understand Koani sometimes.

We're leaving pretty soon to go do a couple of programs in Helena. Koani doesn't want to go. I say let her stay home, but Bruce and Pat insist that she's important to our program. They don't believe that people really come to see me. I think I hear them loading. I'd better go save my place on the bus. Hey, I gotta go. Seee ya!

Love, Indy

A New
Suit of Clothes

May 3, 1995

Finally, I'M GOING TO JETTISON those icky clumps of paint that are all over my ruff. Remember when I wrote about rolling in a puddle of gray paint back in February? At first I thought it was cool, but after a while I got tired of the spiked-hair look. I'm getting rid of it because I'm shedding. Shedding makes me itchy, so it feels good when Pat brushes big clumps of fur out of me. Except sometimes she brushes too hard. Then I have to growl and snap at her. I know you understand because I've heard Pat and Bruce's niece screech and yell when her mom brushes her hair.

Anyway, by the end of May, all my soft underfur will be gone. All I'll have left is long, coarse outer hair, which is called guard hair. Pat says I look like a cartoon wolf during the summer because without my underfur my legs look longer, my body seems more narrow and lanky, and my head appears even bigger. But that's the way wolves are supposed to look when it's warm. You humans take off your big, bulky winter coats during the summer and so do I. Magazines and books only print pictures of us wolves in our winter coats, so most people never see us in our summer coats.

On another subject: I wanted to ask, do you ever get scared that your family would leave you by mistake? I do. Wolves like to know where their families are all the time. We don't like to be alone, so we usually keep pretty good track of each other. I always want to know where at least one packmate is. But sometimes it's such a nice warm day that I fall fast asleep in my outdoor pen. Suddenly, I wake up with this awful feeling that Indy and Bruce and Pat have left without me. I race down the tunnel howling and whimpering and then burst through my swinging door into my living room, still whining and carrying on. Well, one of them is always there, and I'm so relieved that I squeal and wag my tail until they join me in the living room pen. Then we muzzle and join in a group howl to tell each other, and all the world, that we'll always be together. After a while I feel reassured. Then I go back out and take another nap. If I think about it, I don't really believe they'd ever leave me. But sometimes when I wake up from a deep sleep, I'm kind of groggy and not thinking very clearly. What about you?

In two days it's my birthday. The next time you hear from me, I'll be four years old.

Muzzle Nuzzles, Koani

Dog Prison

May 9, 1995

W E CELEBRATED KOANI'S FOURTH BIRTHDAY this weekend. She was born May 5, so she's a Cinco de Mayo baby. Here's a disgustingly cute little story about Koani when she was a tiny baby. Looking at her now, it's hard to imagine her as tiny or cute, but she was once. The first time Pat and Bruce met Koani, you could hold her in one hand. Koani was two weeks old, and her eyes were still closed. Pat held Koani and bottle-fed her. As Koani sucked and chewed on the rubber nipple, her eyes opened. So the very first thing in her life that Koani saw was Pat looking down at her with one of those wonderful Pat-smiles.

I'd already been around for nine months or so when Koani entered the world. That makes me the oldest, which I will always be; there's no way she can get ahead of me. The reason I'm not certain about being nine months older is that Bruce and Pat found me in dog prison, so we don't know exactly when my birthday is.

Pat just looked at what I've written so far and a woebegone look crossed her face. She said, "It's sad we don't know when to celebrate Indy's birthday. But it's because he was a poor little orphaned guy when we got him." The way I look at it, I celebrate a rebirthday on August 17. Not having a birthday is a small price to pay when I think about what could've happened. Here's the story of my rebirthday.

I was in the pen, dog prison, or what you guys call the animal shelter. They busted me for breaking and exiting, third offense, so I

Bruce and Pat found me in dog prison. I was Number 27.

was doing life. Before that, I lived in a trailer park with people who never played with me or took me for walks or anything. They'd pet me on the head, tell me I was cute, and then be gone all day long. I got bored. So I figured out how to open the latch on the gate.

There I was, footloose and fancy-free, when this dogcatcher spotted me. He called me, sounding all nice and sweet. He offered me a dog biscuit, and I thought, "Ain't it great getting out like this?" Then BAM, next thing I knew, this guy grabbed me by the collar, put me in the truck, and hauled me off to dog prison. They locked me up with a bunch of other dogs–none of which, by the way, were near as cute as me.

Here's the part of the story that embarrasses me: I fell for the dogcatcher's trick three times. The first two times, my people bailed me out. But the third time, they couldn't afford to, so I was stuck. And I knew the score, either I got one of the people who visited the animal shelter to like me or it was lights out, end of the game, kick the bucket. However you want to word it, I had to get someone to bail me out or I'd be deader than a doornail.

In dog prison you lose your name and become a number. I was Number 27. I marked my time in a three-by-six-foot cage. Six weeks passed and no dice. Fortunately for me, I'm cute and the people who work at the animal shelter liked me, because it's pretty rare for a dog to last six weeks in dog prison. But, to tell you the truth, I didn't sweat it. I knew I could charm someone enough to get out. But I wasn't in a hurry because I was waiting for the right person.

Then one day, Pat walked in. She looked at me with one of those wonderful Pat-smiles. I jumped up and down. She called me a "popcorn dog" and said, "Oh, you're so cute."

I thought, "Made in the shade, I'm outta here, babe." No dice; she walked out and left me wondering, for the first and only time in my life, that maybe being cute isn't enough.

What I didn't know is that she wanted Bruce to meet me. As it turned out, Bruce was busy that day. They decided to return the next day, which would be August 17.

"Maybe you better call the animal shelter and tell them that you like Number 27," Bruce said. Pat called, but the phone was busy. Then she got involved with something and forgot to try calling again. At three minutes before six o'clock, which is when the animal shelter closed, she suddenly remembered.

"It's a good thing you called," said the woman at the animal shelter. "A bunch of new dogs came in today, and we have to make room for them. Number 27 is at the top of the list to be put to sleep in the morning."

Some people think that was cutting it wicked close. But to me, a miss is as good as a mile. Anyway, that's the story of my rebirthday. It's also part of the reason Bruce and Pat named me Indy. The way Pat puts it, "He qualified to be named after Indiana Jones, the famous movie adventure hero, because he has a wolf for a companion and he escaped certain death by three minutes."

I think it's close to walk time. Hey, I gotta go. Seee ya!

Love, Indy

Brilliant Artist
or
Destructo-Queen?

May 17, 1995

WHAT WOULD YOUR PARENTS DO to you if you ripped a brand new blanket to shreds? If I tore up a blanket–well, I don't even want to think about what would happen. It makes me so nervous my tail won't wag. But Koani shredded a blanket and guess what? Pat calls it ART! Here's the story. After you hear it, tell me what you think about Koani. Is she a brilliant artist or a destructo-queen?

We'd just started our winter road trip, and a few hundred miles south of home Pat realized that Koani's blankey didn't get packed in the van. I know lots of humans think it's silly to give a dog, or in this case a wolf, a blanket to sleep on. They say wolves in the wild don't have blankets. No doubt, but that doesn't mean they wouldn't use one if they had one. Everybody likes to feel comfortable. You don't require a pillow to survive, but I'll bet that you like resting your head on one when you sleep at night.

Pat insisted that Koani needed a blankey, and yes, she realized it was Sunday so there were no secondhand stores open where we could buy an inexpensive blanket, and no it couldn't wait for one night, and so why don't we pull in to that mall? They returned from Penney's with a brand-new pink blankey for Koani. Did they get me

67

anything? Nooooo. But that's okay, I guess, because Pat made me my own special pad with a Batman cover. It's pretty coool.

This new blanket is one of those that feels like there's foam on the inside. Koani settled into a good night's sleep, and in the morning she woke up feeling kind of bored. So she bit the blanket. That felt kind of neat, so she chibble-bit and chewed the blanket some more.

You know those sheets of plastic bubbles that people use to pack fragile things with? And you know how fun it is to pop one of those bubbles and how after you've popped one, you pop another and another and another until they're all popped? Well, that's how Koani got going on her pink, foam-core blankey. A chibble-bite here, some casual chewing there, a dramatic slash down the middle, a tear in the side. Eventually, that blanket became so shredded that it looked like someone had run over it with a lawn mower.

A week later, after Pat had washed the ravaged blanket and hung it out to dry, an artist stopped by to visit. "That's beautiful," she said, pointing to the blanket on the clothesline. "Who is the artist?" Pat explained what had happened. "Magnificent," said the artist, "Koani is a master deconstructionist!"

There are two kinds of artists—constructionists and deconstructionists. Constructionists add things to create art, like a painter brushing paint on a canvas to create a portrait. Deconstructionists take away stuff to create something, like a sculptor who chisels away on a block of marble to create a statue.

"A master deconstructionist whose work cries to be heard," the artist carried on and on. "Those little jagged holes bare testimony to a cross-species sense of fear that torments us all. Look at that bold diagonal slash. The technique she utilized is an obvious statement of an inner anguish allowed momentary escape. And those rips are Koani's way of telling us that technology is a fraud in the face of true nature. Oh, this is a masterpiece!"

Pat smiled and looked as wicked proud as proud can be.

"Looks like a ripped-up blanket," muttered Bruce, "and a wasted $20 at that."

"Koani isn't an artist. She's a blanket vandal. What do you think, artist or spoiled princess?"

Frankly, I agree. The way I see it, Koani isn't an artist. She's a blanket vandal. What do you think, artist or spoiled princess? Hey, I gotta go. Seee ya!

Love, Indy

More Good News and Sad News

May 22, 1995

I CAN'T BELIEVE IT! They're packing the van! We're going someplace. Don't ask me where. Maybe Indy will tell you next week. Since I'm not much into future plans, I'll tell you the big news, which is kind of neat and kind of sad.

Remember a few weeks ago, Indy wrote about finding our coyote friend shot near our place? Well, a few days ago while out on a walk, we headed towards an old den that coyotes used before I was born. It's near where we found the dead coyote. I like to go to the den and sniff and dig. That way it'll be ready in case I ever need it. In fact, over the past few years, I've increased the length of the den a good ten feet. As we neared the den, Indy and I began to get excited because we could smell coyote loud and clear. Of course Pat couldn't smell a thing. (I don't know how you humans survive with such useless noses that provide an utterly insipid sense of smell.) But she got suspicious because of how excited we acted, so she wrapped the leash around a tree and ordered Indy back. Then she peered ahead and saw that the dirt mound at the entrance of the den was all packed down with well-worn trails leading to it.

Now I don't know why, but she wouldn't let us go near. In fact, she unceremoniously dragged me away, muttering that the coyote didn't need me to further complicate her life. Pat led us to a distant hillside where we could observe the entrance. And after a while, you know what happened? A coyote pup crept out! Pretty soon two more crawled out. They chased each other's tails and acted plain silly. Pat said I used to do things like that. I don't believe it, but watching them made me feel kind of warm inside. I like puppies. As for adult canines, unless I met them when I was a pup, I don't care for them. In fact, I'd just as soon beat them up. But pups are a different story. I can get downright goofy with puppies. I really wanted to go see those pups, but Pat was adamant that I couldn't. So in the end we just watched.

Pretty soon, the mother trotted down the path, and all the puppies ran to her. They licked her around the mouth, and you know what that means. But it didn't look like she had much food to give them. Just a mouse or two, not enough for three growing pups. Pat says the coyote will have a hard time feeding the pups now that she's a single mom. I wouldn't blame her if she picked out a juicy little lamb. Would you? Still I hope she doesn't because she'd probably get killed. Maybe someone will shoot her anyway, just for being a coyote–the same reason someone killed her mate, or husband, as you humans would say. That'd be awful. Who'd take care of the puppies then?

It's real neat to have them living by us, but at the same time it's sad because of what happened to their dad. Life's kind of complicated, isn't it?

Muzzle Nuzzles, Koani

Famous
Mountaineers

June 12, 1995

W<small>E'RE</small> BACK! And now I get to tell you the story about the
mountain we climbed while we were in Washington. We not only
set a world's record, we accomplished something nobody has ever
done before! The Wild Sentry team completed the longest and
highest (and most unnecessary) wolf-walk ever. Not only that, we're
the first dog-wolf-human team to climb Whitehorse Mountain. I'll bet
we're the first wolf-human team to climb a mountain anywhere in the
world. Like Bruce said, "Who else would be crazy enough to try?"

Whitehorse stands at the western edge of the Cascade Range
just north of Seattle. From a jungle of fir, cedar, ferns, devil's club,
stinging nettle, alder, and moss, the peak rises to a broad glacial ice
cap out of which the rocky summit juts like a cold tombstone.
(Bruce helped me with that eloquent description; I'd have just said
it was a big, tall mountain.)

Whitehorse is Pat's "family mountain." Her father and his brothers
and sister grew up on a homestead at the foot of Whitehorse. During
the Depression, when they didn't have money to go to the movies,
they entertained themselves by climbing the mountain and exploring
its many secret places. Pat climbed the mountain for the first time
when she was ten and has climbed it many times since then. Bruce
told me that when he and Pat were first getting to know each other,
before they married, Pat took him on a trip up Whitehorse. He set
out expecting a family outing on a high hill and, boy oh boy, was he

surprised–he returned from climbing a huge mountain feeling body-whomped. I would love to have been there to see that.

To reach the summit, you must travel fourteen miles round-trip and climb seven thousand feet–that's more than a mile high! We made an alpine start. That means we headed out at five o'clock in the morning when it was still dark. Up and up and up we hiked until we reached snow, where Bruce, Pat and her cousin Cris put on waterproof boots. Once again, Koani and I noted the canine's superiority over humans; our footwear is good in all conditions.

Eventually we reached High Pass and ate lunch. They gave us vitamin M, which are really M&M candies. I like the red ones best. Next we traversed the glacial ice cap, traversing crevasses and climbing steep slopes. Finally we reached the top. Man, we were wicked high! The backside of Whitehorse drops off suddenly to plunge thousands of feet straight down. It's the kind of place where you don't want to slip. Being that close to such a heavy gravity area made me nervous! The awesome drop beneath her paws even impressed Koani, and she's the kind of wolf who likes to trot right to the edge of a cliff.

You need to remember that for this entire trip, a leash connected Koani to Bruce, Pat or Cris. To begin our descent, we slid down snow slopes doing what's called, in mountaineering terms, a glissade. Bruce started sliding down with Koani running behind him. They made a good team until Koani raced off to the side, which pulled Bruce head over heels until he did a face plant in the snow. I turned my back so he couldn't see me laugh. After he emptied the snow out of his shirt and pants, they started down again.

At one point, I fell into a crevasse and had to rescue myself from its inky depths. Bruce said it was just a little crack in the snow, but what does he know? Three times during the descent, Koani went on strike and lay down in the middle of the path to sleep. As soon as I saw her do that, I did the same. I wasn't tired, of course, but I learned from Koani that it's wise to conserve energy.

Finally, we reached the bottom and the end of the journey. Now I'm happy to report that I finally know who I am! I used to think I

"They made a good team until Koani raced off to the side, which pulled Bruce head over heels."

was a water dog until I hung out with a black lab and learned that water dogs have to actually leap into water and swim after sticks (which is an utterly cold, wet, and stupid thing to do). Then I thought I was a sailor, a real salt-of-the-sea dog until I realized that boats only work in water. I could be a good moose-chasing dog, but Bruce discourages that activity. After being the star of this world-record climb up Whitehorse, I now know that I'm an alpine dog, a mountaineer canine. There's just one thing bad about it–I'm scared of heights. There's also one thing I don't understand: Why do people climb mountains?

Hey, I really need a nap. I gotta go. Seee ya!

Love, Indy

Another
Free Lunch

July 17, 1995

We HAD BIG EXCITEMENT this week! Last Tuesday we headed out on a walk late in the afternoon like we always do. We'd gone about a quarter mile and crossed an irrigation ditch when I smelled something in a thicket of fir trees. Sniff, sniff, sniff, and then I plunged in, pulling Pat unceremoniously with me (for some reason she never wants to go into thick brush–no sense of adventure, I guess).

Suddenly, there was treasure–a dead deer, but so fresh that flies hadn't even found it. Only the innards and a little bit of the hindquarter were gone. The carcass was covered with sticks and pine needles. Then I picked up a smell that made the hair on the back of my neck stand up. Mountain lion! I know Pat realized that a lion killed the deer because she started yelling for Indy as she looked up in the trees.

You might recall that Indy did time in prison (or what you guys call the dog pound). He told me all about it. If someone locked me up like that, I'd go crazy. It's amazing that he's not more confused than he is. As it is, he doesn't have a grip on who or what he is–he has an identity problem. Whatever seems appropriate at the moment is what he thinks he is. I'm sure at that moment he saw himself as a cougar hound. When he finally returned, she told him to keep close because a mountain lion would love a little fatty grub like him. Of course, he didn't pay any attention to Pat. He's convinced he can whip any cat there is, but she made him stay with us anyway.

She tried to pull me away from the deer carcass. NO WAY! I'm not stupid–I know cougars can be dangerous, especially when you're thieving from one of their kills. But I figured that if I could get away with it, this was free meat. So I stood there with my hackles up, looking all around. I grabbed a leg and pulled the deer towards a clearing. A twig snapped! I jumped straight up in the air and surveyed the area with hyper-alert attention. When Pat saw me jump, she jumped and whirled around too. Then she laughed because she realized that I caused that twig to snap when I stepped on it. I calmed down and went back to work on the deer. Finally, I tugged it out in the open, and we all felt better. I settled down to eat. The cougar had left the very best part: the antlers, which were still in velvet.

Yummy! I crunched every last bit of them. Then I ate some meat, but I wasn't really very hungry, so we left. Of course, I put out signs that say, "This is Koani's meat. Disturb at Your Own Risk." I do that by urinating. Then I scratch with my front feet so that big clods of grass and dirt fly behind me.

However, my warning didn't do much good. The next day, the deer was half gone. Four days later, we found only three lower legs. I'm not certain if it was the cougar that returned, but the deer definitely didn't go to waste.

I think I'd better sign off for now. Pat and Bruce are packing the van, so we're headed out on another trip.

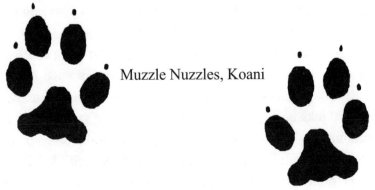

Muzzle Nuzzles, Koani

I Lost
My Mind

July 25, 1995

I'M BUMMED. I kind of messed up, just a little bit. I mean it's not a HUGE deal. But I admit, my behavior was less than stellar. We were on a wolf walk. Out in the meadows, the morning sun felt warm on my back; in the shade of pine trees, the air felt cool and perfect. Little did I know, as we ambled up the dirt road towards home, that I'd lose my mind.

We rounded the edge of an aspen grove that borders a meadow of tall, dewy grass, and that's when I first picked up the scent. I put my nose in the air and followed the smell. At that point, I was just curious, that's all. I looked back and saw Bruce and Koani way behind me, the way they always are, Koani sniffing a stalk of knapweed where a deer had probably brushed against it a week ago. BORING.

The breeze shifted and suddenly, I mainlined the smell. I'm talking about a heavy-duty odoriferous hit and the smell–like neon–said ELK! An elk real close, right down in the meadow, not even fifty feet away.

I don't know if this kind of thing ever happens to you or not–where you know you're not supposed to do something and you do it anyway. It's like a space alien gets inside of your brain and says, "Forget about what mom and dad told you. What do they know? You want to do it, you need to do it, so just do it." And I did. I plunged into the meadow moving faster than a laser, straight to where I smelled elk.

The elk leaped to her hooves and raced across the meadow wild-eyed and snorting fear. Oh, it felt wicked good to run flat-out fast as I could, the tall grass in my face, the dew cool and wet against my nose. It just doesn't get much better than that.

Bruce says he saw me launch and started bellowing like a rogue elephant, screaming at the top of his lungs for me to STOP! I guess he must've been telling the truth because Pat says that she heard him from a quarter mile away. But here's the weird part–and it's the honest truth, cross my paws and hope to die–I never heard him. He wasn't even a blip on my radar screen.

Well, I chased that elk across the creek and so far into the forest that I bet she didn't stop until she reached the Pacific Ocean. Suddenly, I gained control of my mind. I knew I was in trouble. I crossed the stream again, which flowed pretty full. By the time I reached the other side, I was soaked and wondering how I'd made it across so easily the first time. I returned to the house with my tail between my legs. Koani greeted me like a hero and wanted to know all about my grand adventure. Bruce treated me like an airheaded Lost Boy. He didn't say a word–I'm not sure if he had a hoarse throat from yelling or if he was mad beyond words. I think he was mad.

He gave me a lecture. I sulked off to pout beneath the table. A while later, he found me and told me that he still loved me. I was glad to hear that because sometimes I worry that they'll ship me back to dog prison where they found me. He told me that I'm NEVER to chase animals, especially elk, deer, cows, and horses. "There are people who would shoot you for doing that," he said. "Not only that, those animals could stomp the stuffing out of you if they wanted to. And that includes moose too, you Boy of Little Brains."

He just doesn't understand how difficult it is not to do something that feels so good. Once, I was with some kids who used crayons to draw beautiful flowers, on their bedroom walls. The kids loved drawing the flowers, and I thought the drawings looked cool. Everything seemed great until their parents walked in.

So, I've been working real hard at behaving. Sometimes it's hard. Would I chase an elk again? That's a difficult question. I sure didn't plan on doing it last time; it just happened. I really don't have a good excuse. I have to be careful not to lose my mind.

Now I've got a question for you. Have you ever done something that you knew you weren't supposed to do even as you started doing it? And here's the really hard question. If you knew better, why did you do it anyway? Boy oh boy, the mysteries of life. I better lay out in the sun and think about this. Hey, I gotta go. Seee ya!

Love, Indy

The Bogus Pet Wolf

July 31, 1995

W<small>E JUST RETURNED FROM</small> doing programs in Noxon, Montana, and Hope and Clark Fork, Idaho. It was way too hot. The heat almost made me like the van because it's air-conditioned. Besides being hot, flies flew all around and drove me absolutely crazy. Pat and Bruce think it looks silly for a wolf to hunt flies, but their incessant buzzing is so aggravating! Pat and Bruce also say it serves me right to be bothered by flies. According to them, flies are attracted to me because of all the icky things I roll in.

A funny thing happened on this last trip. It was during one of the programs. Pat got Indy and me out of the van and was leading us past some cars, when a dog in one of the cars started barking at me. He was a big, gray dog with a big chest and a tail that curled up over his back. He stuck his head out the window, wagged his tail and grinned at us. I, of course, raised my hackles, snarled and tried to leap for his throat. I am, after all, a wolf. Wolves don't like strange canines.

After the program, a man said that he owned a wolf. Well, his "wolf" turned out to be the dog we'd seen in the car. There's no way that canine was a wolf. Clue number one: When the dog stepped out of the car, anyone with eyes could see that his dainty little paws weren't those of a wolf. Clues number two and three: He had a cute, curly tail and a broad chest. Wolves don't have either. Clue number four: He barked. Wolves hardly ever bark–only if we're super alarmed. I've never barked. I suppose I could, but there's never been a good reason. Clue number five: He acted friendly towards me. That's not wolfish behavior. Wolves only like family members–you know, pack mates. The final clue: He was sitting in the back seat of a car, but he hadn't ripped holes in the upholstery or chewed up the steering wheel or even pulverized the window visors. No self-respecting wolf would sit in a car all alone and not tear it apart (it's absolutely ridiculous to think one would)!

Anyway, it's a good lesson that you shouldn't believe everything you hear. If your friends say their dog is a wolf, or mostly wolf, but it rides around in the back of the truck, is nice to cats, and comes when called, it's NOT a wolf. We wolves cause big problems when we're kept in captivity. Just ask Bruce and Pat. I'm a teacher, not a pet. One of the things I teach is that wolves are not good pets!

Muzzle Nuzzles, Koani

Attitude Adjustment

August 8, 1995

THE LAST TIME I WROTE, I felt depressed because Bruce had scolded me for chasing an elk. That put me into a blue-funk, which caused me to pout, and that can be dangerous because when I pout, I REALLY get into it. Putting on a good pout takes the skill of an award-winning actor–every muscle in my body, every move I make has to whimper, "Woe is me!" My shoulders and back slump as if I'm about to melt, my mouth droops into a frown that looks like I'm about to drool, my tail hangs down, my head lowers, and–with the saddest, tear-glazed, puppy-dog eyes–I peer up every once in a while to make sure someone is paying attention. (What's the use of pouting if no one notices?) Without uttering a word, everything about me says, "Nobody loves me. I guess I might as well go eat worms." Does this ever happen to you?

Anyway, the reason a serious pout can be dangerous is that it's easy to forget I'm acting. Sometimes my act works so well that I'm even convinced I'm in a blue-funk, like I've dug a hole and can't climb out. Big bummer. When that happens, I have to shake myself hard enough to snap out of it and remind myself the situation isn't that bad. "Things could be a lot worse," I tell myself. "What would the intrepid adventurer Indiana Jones think if he saw you pouting like a little puppy? Get a grip, Indy, you're a big dog."

Then I start feeling better, little by little. And I get to thinking about where I've been, what I've done, and where I'm going. You see, I've been down and out–literally at the end of my rope–but I hung in there. As I realize how far I've come, I suddenly find a grin on my muzzle, and life is good again.

I once had a pretty rough life, as I've told you before. You've probably known dogs that lived most of their lives in a yard or even worse, cooped up in a kennel or chained to a tree. Their people seldom take them for walks or play with them. (Why do humans want a dog in the first place if they're just going to ignore it? They may as well have a houseplant.) Well, I was one of those dogs once; I sat in a little yard all day and night with nothing to do and nobody to do it with.

The boredom was more than I could handle, so I learned how to open the gate, broke out, and took to roaming. Being a street dog led to trouble and landed me in dog prison. I did my time and returned to the same old dismal situation I'd escaped from. I became what they call a repeat offender. Finally, the people I'd lived with said, "That's it, we're not bailing him out anymore," and I ended up on death row. With only minutes to spare, Bruce and Pat showed up to rescue me. On my release papers, it says, "Escape artist. This dog needs a high fence with a secure gate!"

No way! I just needed something to do and somebody to do it with. Look at me now! I'm a pillar of the community. I travel to schools and teach kids. I live with a wolf. Koani thinks I'm the best thing going. Bruce and Pat believe I'm the cutest dog in the world. Of course they're all correct. I've got fans all over the West, and pretty soon we're headed back East so more people can meet me. When I trotted onstage in San Francisco, I got a standing ovation. I've appeared in newspapers and TV and been on radio–including the *Pea Green Boat,* the very best radio program in the universe. I bet they'll want to make a movie about me. The title could be "Indy: An American Success Story–From Dog Prison to the Smithsonian." After all, I'm a star. I'm not bragging here; these are just the facts.

No more pouting for me. I'm a dog of action. I've got places to see, things to do, and people to meet. Hey, I gotta go. Seee ya!

Love, Indy

Ms. Chloe Dog Cook Goes to Canine Camp

August 21, 1995

FINALLY, INDY AND KOANI let me write another letter to you. It's been so long you probably don't even remember me. I'm Ms. Chloe Dog Cook, the black-and-white spotted Great Dane. I also happen to be Indy and Koani's best friend. I met them back when they were young pups and I was a mature two-year-old. Now I'm six and getting a little stiff when I wake up in the morning. But if you allow me a little time to warm up, I'm still plenty fast.

Last week, a woman I'd never seen before came to the door of our house in Missoula. I remained suspicious until she said, "Chloe, I'm taking you to see Koani!" Those are the magic words! I pushed past her, ran out through the door, and leapt into the first open car I saw. An hour later, I jumped out of the car and charged up the path to Koani's pen. Koani always goes nuts when she sees me, whimpering, whining, and kissy-facing. Indy jumps up and down and tries to grab me by the neck in his excitement. The only trouble is he's too short so he just bounces off me. It's BIG FUN being welcomed like that!

My family says I'm at a summer camp for canines. We play and lie in the sun and chew on bones. Every day we go on two long walks and explore the woods. My buddies show me all the new treasures they've discovered since I last visited, and then we get into fights over them. Koani doesn't share very well. Even if she hasn't played with something or chewed on a bone for a month, as soon as I'm interested in it, she tries to grab it from me. But that's Koani. You

"Koani always goes nuts when she sees me, whimpering, whining, and kissy-facing."

have to understand that she's a wolf and wolves are just that way. In the wild they have to be pretty possessive or they might starve to death. Have you ever not wanted to share your toys, even though you weren't playing with them? It's sort of like that, I guess.

One of the neatest things they showed me this time was the dead calf Koani found a couple of months ago. Too coool! Koani and I played tug of war with it until she got too serious. Then after a while, we both rolled in it, and now we smell just alike, so that makes us best friends again.

Tomorrow Pat's taking me back home, and Indy and Koani are going to begin a long trip–they're doing something called the Great Crossing. They'll be gone almost three months! It makes me sad to think about it, so mostly I don't.

 Respectfully and Responsibly Yours
Love, Ms. Chloe Dog Cook

Packing for a Big Road Trip

August 31, 1995

I DON'T HAVE MUCH TIME to write. Bruce and Pat are madly packing. From all the things they're stuffing in the van, I think we're about to embark on a BIG adventure. All summer long, I've heard them talk of the Great Crossing and a Road Trip to the East Coast. From what I can see, I think it's a happening thing. But still, I get a little worried at times like this because I don't want to be left behind. OH, there goes Bruce carrying a box to the van. I gotta go.

False alarm. You never know when they're going to take off, and I have to make sure to save myself a place on the bus. You wouldn't believe all the stuff Pat and Bruce are taking. Right now, the weather is hot so they have to pack summer clothes like shorts, lightweight pants and shirts. But since we won't be back until mid-November, they also need warm clothes and rain gear and . . . OH, there goes Pat to the van, I might have to sign off for now.

She walked back into the house, so I'll write some more; but I've got my eye on the door. You wouldn't believe all the shoes they're taking! They packed running shoes and hiking boots for taking Koani and me on walks, rubber boots for rainy days, nice shoes for presenting programs, and even Sorrels in case we run into snow.

Here we see another case of canine superiority over humans. People have to pack all kinds of stuff to travel–clothes, shoes, sleeping bags, books, tapes, and more. What do Koani and I need? What we're wearing is enough, and we wouldn't dream of putting shoes on our feet. We have our food bowls. I've got a pad Pat made for me that's pretty cool because she used Batman material. Koani has her blankey. (She's too immature to have a pad; she'd only rip it to shreds, which is what she tries to do to my pad whenever she gets ahold of it.) She also has a fold-up portable wolf house to shelter her from the rain; I get to sleep in the van. And that's it. We're easy. OH, there goes Bruce.

I'm back again. But I'm getting tired of running to and from the van. I'm going to sit in the driver's seat of the van; that way I'll know when we're taking off, and they won't forget me. Hey, I gotta go. Seee ya!

Love, Indy

The Great Crossing

September 4, 1995

WE PASSED THE HALFWAY POINT in the Great Crossing. Right now we're driving through Indiana. They named the state after me, which was a nice thing for them to do, but why didn't they name Montana after me instead? After all, that's where I live–most of the time.

The middle of America is HUGE. We have been driving and driving and driving for hours and hours, and the flatlands go on and on and on. Every once in a while, I'll see something that reminds me of home, like a barn with trees around it, and my eyes drift up, expecting to see mountains in the background; but there aren't any. The last mountains we saw were the Black Hills way back on the western side of South Dakota, and that was days ago. You know the other thing that's missing out here on the Great Crossing? There aren't any places where people are free to visit, hike, camp, or play–I think Bruce calls those places federal lands, which are lands owned by all the people in America. Out here it looks like a monstrously big farm, with mile after mile of cows and corn and soybeans. You can't pull off the road and camp like you can in a national forest or have a picnic beside a stream like you can in a national park.

While doing programs in the Rockies and the Southwest, I've heard a lot of adults whine that it's awful that the federal government requires them to pay attention to rules when they're using public lands. They think they should be free to do whatever they want to do, and blah, blah, blah. Well, if they think it's so bad in Montana or Wyoming or Idaho, they should move to Iowa or Indiana or Illinois, where they wouldn't have a thing to complain about because there isn't any public land. It's all private land: farm after farm after farm, all with signs that say, "No Trespassing, Keep Out."

Right now we're in Lafayette, Indiana, where we're staying with friends who used to live in Montana. They have a cute little girl named Emily who likes to pet me. Lad lives here too; he's a chocolate lab. Lad loves to swim, and where he used to live he could swim whenever he wanted to. He misses that a lot, but at least here he can chase fireflies, which are bugs that light up in the night. That sounds pretty cool. I hope I get to see some. Tomorrow we'll do a program at Purdue University about how wolves and dogs are similar in some ways and different in others. Then we continue the Great Crossing up into Maine. Something had better happen pretty soon because I'm bored with sitting in the van. It's starting to get dark so I'm going to see if I can find some fireflies.

Hey, I gotta go. Seee ya!

Love, Indy

Attack of the Killer Umbrellas

September 9, 1995

A COUPLE DAYS AGO I barely escaped the Attack of the Killer Umbrellas. Pat and Bruce say I'm exaggerating, that I allowed irrational fears to get the better of me. Let me tell you the story, and you can decide for yourself. We were at the Common Ground Fair in Maine. The Common Ground Fair is like fairs anywhere except everything's healthy—they don't sell cotton candy or anything with white sugar or white flour, so all the kids go around sucking on little plastic bears filled with honey. You can't buy coffee either, so all the adults go around with that fuzzy look you see on your parents before they've downed their morning cup of coffee. You know what I mean.

Anyway, we presented programs at the fair, and between programs I hung out with Indy and Pat or Bruce or my new uncle, Steve, who I just met and who's a great guy. [Editor's translation: He feeds Koani lots of dog biscuits.] We sat in a grassy area between a building and the big fence that surrounds the fairgrounds. On the other side of the fence, lots of people were walking down the sidewalk on their way to the entrance gate. That's okay; I could live with that. As long as they don't crowd in, I can deal with people. Quite a few of them stopped to talk or ask questions. Everyone commented on my naturally noble and wolfish beauty—which is to be expected. Indy always tried to horn in and get them to pay attention to him, but he's just a dog.

Anyway, things were just fine. Pat and Bruce wandered off to watch the sheep dog demonstration or something silly like that. They seemed quite happy because Steve stayed with Indy and me, and that gave them some time away together. Sometimes they want to go places without me and Indy; both of us find this very difficult to understand.

So there we were, Indy snoozing on the grass, Uncle Steve talking to people as I lay on my blankey, attached to my cable run, watching the people watch me. Rain began to fall. I didn't mind; it wasn't a hard rain. All of a sudden, from out of the top of people's heads, sticks grew and then POP, the top blossomed into something like the biggest mushroom I've ever seen. And then the thing descended over the head and swallowed it. Too weird and totally SCAARRY! I heard a woman call the thing an umbrella just before it swallowed her head. I paced and panted. I rolled my eyes and quivered and quaked. Umbrellas popped up everywhere and swallowed people headfirst.

Wherever I looked, umbrella heads milled about mindlessly. I realized that soon they would crash through the fence, and it would be all over–an umbrella would swallow my head. Indy just lay there. He may be cute (for a dog) but he's not too bright, and when it comes to assessing danger, you can't trust his judgment.

Fortunately, no umbrellas swallowed Steve's head, but other than that he was worthless. I had to rely on my instincts and the wealth of knowledge contained in my brain. I recalled an old wolf proverb: "When the going gets weird, it's time to get going." I pulled and tugged at my cable. I gasped for air and stared bug-eyed. I ran back and forth. [Editor's note: To put it mildly, Koani panicked.]

Finally Pat and Bruce arrived. They unhooked me from my cable and I rocketed off, with Bruce flying behind me like a balloon attached to a runaway locomotive. Luckily, we spied a little building that didn't have any windows. We dashed inside. Bruce slammed the door behind us. I hid in a corner and waited for umbrella heads to ram the door down. Eventually, I realized that we'd successfully evaded them. At least, none of them tried to come in and swallow our heads. After a while, Pat opened the door. I peered out. The bright sunshine made me blink. Lots of people wandered about hither and thither. But the umbrella heads had disappeared. I think the sun killed them the same way it makes mushrooms shrivel up and vampires turn to dust.

Following that narrow escape, we visited the edge of the continent. I stood atop a cliff and gazed eastward. There was nothing but water for as far as I could see. The breeze carried the smell of ocean, and when we walked down to the shore, the water even tasted like sea water. But I'm used to seeing the ocean stretch out to the west, not the east. Pat explained that this was an entirely different ocean. "That's the Atlantic," she said, "and this is as far from Montana as you're going to get on this trip." Does that mean we're heading home? I sure hope so. Montana isn't good habitat for umbrellas, is it?

Now at programs, Pat and Bruce talk about the attack of the umbrella heads and cite it as another reason why wolves don't make good pets. They say we're neophobic, which means we get scared and freak out at anything new and different. That may be true, but there's a good reason for it–I'm still alive, aren't I? If it hadn't been for me, we'd all be in some umbrella head's stomach by now–which brings to mind another wolf proverb: "No fear is so small that you can't run away from it."

Muzzle Nuzzles, Koani

Watch Out
for Rex!

October 21, 1995

We PRESENTED A PROGRAM in a huge city that people call the Big Apple. Where they got that name is a mystery to me because the place is completely covered with tall buildings, asphalt, and concrete–an apple tree couldn't grow there if it tried. Maybe they grow apples on top of those tall buildings.

We ended up in an underground parking lot beneath a massive museum–I think Bruce called it the American Museum of Natural History–and you'd never believe what they keep there! Inside the museum, I saw bones bigger than a horse or cow or even a moose for that matter, and I'm talking about just ONE BONE, not the whole skeleton. These bones were so big that not even Koani would be able to chew on one. I tried, but a museum guard got pretty upset and chased me away, which was okay because that bone didn't have a bit of taste to it at all. It was like biting on a rock.

Now these bones, when put together, form the skeleton of an absolutely, unimaginably super-gigantic animal with a head as big as a car and teeth so long and sharp they make Koani's teeth look pitiful. (Don't tell Koani I said that!) To an animal that big, you wouldn't even be a mouthful, and if it ate me, it would be about like you eating a grape.

The animal was named Rex. I've heard of dogs named Rex, and if this is how big Rex dogs grow, then I don't ever want to meet one! I'd take fighting with a moose any day over tangling with a Rex.

"The unimaginably, super-gigantic animal was named Rex."

Imagine trying to toss a stick for a dog that big; the stick would have to be the size of a telephone pole. What if you taught it to do tricks like lie down and roll over? If you didn't watch out, it might roll over you and leave you flatter than a pancake. And imagine cleaning up after an animal that big. I don't think a Rex would make a very good pet. As far as I'm concerned, they can keep Rexes in museums.

Something else happened that I couldn't believe. Bruce and Pat didn't take me or Koani to see an opera called *Don Giovanni.* They got all dressed up in fancy clothes and went back into that big city and left Koani and me with a canid sitter. Koani pointed out that if this were a formal occasion, she'd fit right in because of her long-tailed black coat. Pat said that Koani would get restless sitting in one place, and besides there weren't canines or ANY animals in the opera, so Koani wouldn't find it interesting. Now, how can anyone find an opera interesting if it doesn't have animals in it? Bruce told me that I couldn't go because I'd probably run up on the stage and steal the show, which would make the opera singers feel bad. He's right. If I'd been there, people would've wanted to see me instead of the opera; that's just the way things are, I can't help it.

Pretty soon it'll be Halloween. People here in the East get into Halloween in a big way. What are you going to be for Halloween? Hey, a word of advice: If you ever hear that there's a dog named Rex around, stay inside. Hey, I gotta go. Seee ya!

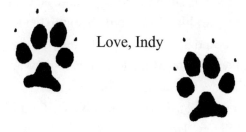

Love, Indy

From
Sleepy Hollow
to Central Park

October 30, 1995

LAST WEEK, WE DROVE THE VAN into a big boat and set sail on storm-tossed seas. Maybe a Labrador Retriever or some gooney water dog like that would've enjoyed crossing the ocean during a storm with waves that crashed over the side of the ship and onto the van–but not me and not Koani. You'd truly have to be a dog of little brains to find pleasure in that kind of thing.

On the other side of the ocean, we did programs in the Peabody Museum at Yale. [Editor's note: We crossed Long Island Sound from New York to Connecticut, not the ocean.] Bruce and Pat were pretty pleased with themselves for giving a lecture at Yale University to a bunch of college students studying to be scientists, which meant that the students tried to act like they were so sophisticated and wicked smart that nothing could get them excited. But you should have seen them when Koani and I entered the lecture hall–they laughed, giggled, and sighed just like everybody else who sees me.

After that we returned to Tarrytown, which is (and I bet you didn't know this) where Sleepy Hollow is located. In case you've forgotten, Sleepy Hollow is where the Headless Horseman rides on Halloween Night. Squirrelwood Forest is also in Tarrytown, and I love it there because it's my favorite squirrel-chasing place in the world.

Fortunately, we left Tarrytown just before Halloween, and that's fine by me. Even though there's not much that scares me, I'd rather not meet up with the Headless Horseman.

Later, Pat and Bruce drove right smack-dab into Manhattan; that's the New York City island full of skyscrapers and what Bruce called "white-knuckle traffic." He muttered a few other words to describe the traffic, but I won't repeat them. The cars crammed together bumper to bumper, taxis zoomed in front of us, people ignored traffic lights, horns honked, and general chaotic gridlock craziness surrounded us. I saw a few dogs too, and I felt sorry for them. Some of them wore silly sweaters or ribbons, and their people pulled them around on short leashes. Most embarrassing of all, the poor dogs had to poop on the sidewalk.

Finally, we stopped and–I couldn't believe it–took a walk in a HUGE city park. They call it Central Park because it's right there in the center of all that concrete and pavement. Smack-dab in the middle of a mondo city there's a beautiful park. AMAZING! Contrary to all the stories you hear about Central Park, no gangs attacked us and no muggers robbed us. Both Koani and I enjoyed our walk, and the only thing that happened is that people stopped and pointed at me, which is something I've learned to expect–that's what happens when you're the cutest dog in the world. It comes with the territory.

The Smithsonian in Washington, D.C. is next. I guess I've come a long way for a dog who sat on Death Row in Missoula's Dog Prison. Bruce and Pat call me an American success story. Hey, I gotta go. Seee ya!

Love, Indy

Washington, D.C. and Montana Politicians

November 8, 1995

WE'RE ON OUR WAY HOME! I can hardly wait to get back. I'll get to run around in my pen without a leash holding me back. I'll get to have my collar off and run around bare-necked. Dinner will once again consist of deer and elk. When we travel, I have to settle for cow and chicken meat (and here's the yucky part, someone wraps that meat with plastic). I hope it won't be long until my friend Ms. Chloe Dog Cook comes to visit. Even if she doesn't come to Gopher Ranch Estate, I'm going to visit her because I'm doing a program in Missoula at Sentinel High School.

One of our last programs was at the Mall in Washington, D.C. When I first heard about it, I thought the program would be at one of those places where people go shopping; but it wasn't. The Mall is a huge, parklike place outdoors with big statues and lots of different kinds of museums that are all called Smithsonians. We did four programs at one of the Smithsonians, which was called the Museum of Natural History. Then we took a walk in the Mall. Bruce photographed us in front of a big, white house, and he said Socks might like to see that photo. [Editor's note: Socks is the cat that lives with the Clinton family.] He took pictures of us beside a huge, bearded stone man sitting in a chair. This statue was located near a monstrous building with lots of steps and a big white dome on top. I marked the bottom step with my scent, just for good measure. But what interested Indy and me more than anything else was chasing

"One of our last programs was at the Mall in Washington, D.C."

ducks and geese on the little lakes (Pat and Bruce called them "reflecting pools") at the Mall. There are way too many ducks and geese swimming around in those reflecting ponds. They need a few good wolves around that place to thin the flocks.

Speaking of which, I couldn't agree more with Montana legislators. Last winter they introduced a resolution to the state legislature saying that if the federal government reintroduced wolves to Yellowstone National Park, then the government should also reintroduce wolves to Washington, D.C., San Francisco, and Central Park in New York City. They're right. All those places are overrun with squirrels, pigeons, and dogs, and we wolves could help!

When Pat and Bruce and Indy and I visited Central Park, I found a little grassy knoll, lay down, and just watched all the amazing things: dogs in all forms and colors, people in all shapes and sizes. And surrounding the whole park were buildings that stood way taller than the trees. I wonder what those people and dogs would have thought if they'd known a wolf was watching them?

Muzzle Nuzzles, Koani

Of Slush and Fur

December 12, 1995

I CAN'T BELIEVE THIS YUCKY WEATHER! There's only one word I can think of to describe it: SILLY! This morning, Pat came downstairs and prepared for the walk. Of course, I got all excited like I always do. But then I noticed her putting on rubber boots, rain pants, and a storm parka, and I thought to myself, "I've got a bad feeling about this." Pat opened the door and sure enough, rain poured from a soggy, gray sky. Rain in December when it should be snowing. It's just SILLY.

I turned to go back indoors, but Pat had already closed the door. We headed out, rain sluicing down on us, turning all our beautiful snow into wet, heavy slush. I definitely prefer light, fluffy snow to this gunk. Last Sunday, when I ran outside and saw a few inches of fresh, powdery snow, I felt delirious. I roared around in it until I noticed snow on the pond; then I ran over, leaped off the end of the dock, and skidded a wicked long ways across the ice. Next I rolled onto my back and wallowed and wiggled in the snow. It felt wonderful. Bruce calls

105

me a Big Sky Snow Roller because I like doing that so much. But now rolling in what little snow we have left would be about as much fun as rolling in the remains of a snow cone someone dropped in the dirt.

Koani doesn't mind the rain as much as I do unless it pours on us for a couple of weeks like it did in California last winter. Long-term rain depresses her, and she mopes around wearing a real hangdog, dejected look on her mug. (Fortunately she didn't have to float around in Noah's Ark.) Her good attitude towards occasional rain isn't because she's tough or anything like that, it's because she came equipped with fur that sheds the rain. It'd be like you being born with a raincoat. (Come to think of it, you are born with waterproof skin. However, you're always covering it with clothes that soak up rain.) We all know that dogs, especially dogs like me, are superior to wolves. I mean, there's no doubt about it. But, every once in a while, I notice things about Koani that leave me wondering.

Fortunately, those rare moments of uncertainty pass quickly. I do have to admit Koani's fur is impressive, with its soft, downy undercoat covered by long, stiff guard hairs. To give you an idea of how well that fur works, when we got home from walking around in the woods for an hour and a half, I was soaked even after I shook. Koani shook and was only damp. In the winter–well, I guess it's winter now, but I mean when it's REALLY winter, with snow and ice and frosty days–I've seen her sleep outside with snow falling. Her fur is so thick and does such a good job of insulating her that the snow doesn't even melt; it just piles up until she's covered with inches of snow.

Don't get the idea that I'm at all envious of Koani in any way, not a guy like me who has so much going for him. Besides, Koani needs something to be proud of.

You're probably wondering what I want for Christmas. FOOD. Lots of food would suit me just fine: meaty bones to chew, milk bone biscuits to munch, a bit of ice cream to lick up–ahhh, yes. I'm not a garbage hound, though. There are things I don't like. For instance, tofu, broccoli, grapefruit–and listen to that rain. Yuck, that's something else I don't care for–rain when it should be snowing. Can't somebody do something about that?

I'm going to stretch out on the couch, take a nap, and dream of a white Christmas. Hey, I gotta go. Seee ya!

 Love, Indy

A Tour of
the Wolf Van

January 8, 1996

IN A COUPLE OF WEEKS, we'll be off again on another road trip to present The Indy Dog Show and to spread sunshine in hearts where darkness, gloom, and despair once reigned. To tell you the truth, I'm looking forward to a change, a little excitement, lights, action, and crowded auditoriums filled with people who want to see me. After all, nothing much is going on around here, and I'm a little bored. We did see a fox the other day, and there have been lots of deer and an occasional elk herd nearby. A moose roams the woods, but Bruce manages to steer us away from her–what a chicken! Plus, Pat was gone for a week, so Koani and I were stuck with Bruce. I don't want to come off sounding rude, but having only one human around can be pretty boring. I think it's best to have two humans, preferably a male and a female close to the same age, because they can entertain each other when you want to nap. Two humans seem to be happier, provided they get along like my two do. And like I've always said, a happy human is a more playful, frisky, and fun human. But anyway, I'm looking forward to setting off on a new adventure.

People often ask questions about our trips: How do we travel? What kind of car do we drive? Where do we stay? Do we ever end up in a motel? Is it hard to find places to walk the wolf? Well, to start with, we travel in the wolf van. Bruce and Pat named it the Great White Whale. Actually it's a Dodge Ram van, which means, as I once heard Bruce say, it comes factory-equipped with a rotten transmission (it completely broke down and stranded us in Washington for a week). The van, as you might have guessed from its name, is white; it's also extra-long and has an extended top. Koani's wire kennel fills most of the van. On top of the kennel, there's a sleeping platform for the humans. In the midsection you'll find a set of cupboards, and beneath them a countertop with shelves below. My pad is on the countertop; that's where I kick back and hang out while traveling. That's another difference between me and Koani—when it comes to traveling, I know how to chill; Koani's always panting and hyperalert. If the van hits a little bump in the road, she jumps to her feet and stares out the window as if we're headed over a cliff and she might be able to prevent it.

The bottom of my pad is supposed to be skidproof. But I remember a time while winding our way along a mountain road in Arizona when it didn't stop me from skidding. The curves on that road were so wicked sharp that as the front of the van finished a turn, you could look to the side and see the back of the van just starting around. On one of those curves, which we headed into a bit too fast if you ask me, my pad shot off the countertop. For one wide-eyed nanosecond, my pad (with me on top) hovered in midair like a magic carpet, and then it plunged to the floor. Crash! So much for the pad being skidproof.

To continue our tour of the van, next there's the cab, up front where Bruce and Pat sit. Between the two seats there's a cooler where they keep meat for Koani, food for humans, and treats for me. On top of the cooler is another pad, and guess who spends quite a bit of time stretched out there getting petted and scratched. Me, of course. Koani wouldn't be able to lie still long enough. She'd chew something or shred something else or do some crazy stunt that would cause the van to swerve off the road, crash through the safety rail, rocket over the edge of a cliff, plunge into the sea, and sink to the

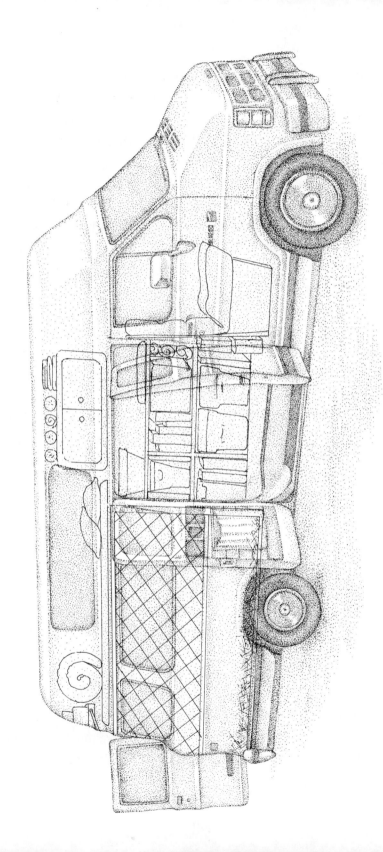

We travel in a van named the Great White Whale.

ocean bottom, where we'd probably have to wait a year before a submarine rescued us. So now you see why Koani has to travel in a kennel and I don't. Next time, I'll tell you about staying in motels and our special equipment for camping out. Hey, I gotta go. Seee ya!

 Love, Indy

Umbrella Slayer!

January 16, 1996

Do you remember how the umbrella heads terrorized me at that fair in Maine? Well, I got revenge this week! I absolutely, unequivocally, flat-out killed an umbrella. I feel no guilt or remorse either. In fact, I feel great. Here's what happened: Pat and Bruce have (I should say HAD) a black umbrella. For some reason, they brought the horrible thing into my pen and walked around with it. They said, "We have to habituate Koani to umbrellas." Well, I'm not sure what "habituate" means but it didn't sound good. [Editor's note: According to the *American Heritage Dictionary*, "habituate" means "to accustom by frequent repetition or prolonged exposure." We thought that if we walked around Koani's pen with an umbrella for a few minutes every day Koani would get used to it.]

I kept a close eye on that ugly umbrella whenever it came near. Then they started leaving it next to my pen instead of making it go back in the house with them. Can you imagine how spooky that felt? Eventually I realized that the umbrella slept most of the time; if Bruce and Pat weren't around, it didn't move. So one day I reached through the fence with my paw to see what it would do, but I couldn't touch it. The umbrella just sat there. I decided that maybe rain brought umbrellas to life and they hibernated the rest of the time.

Well, that's how things stood for quite a while. But last week, Pat woke the umbrella up and exercised it a little bit. Then she laid it down to sleep near the edge of my pen. I looked at the umbrella and it looked a little closer to the fence than usual.

I watched it for an hour to make sure it was asleep and not just pretending. I crept up and poked my paw at it. Next, I worked up all of my courage and actually touched it! Scary! I leaped back, but it didn't do anything. I watched and waited and finally I stuck my paw out again, dragged it close, and grabbed it with my jaws!

To make a long story short, by the time Pat returned to the pen, all that remained was a skeleton and a few scraps of skin. Now I have a new nickname: "Umbrella Slayer." Pretty cool, huh? Next time I see an umbrella, I'm going to say, "I'm rough, I'm tough, and I've had enough!"

If you've got any troublesome umbrellas hanging around, who ya' gonna call? Umbrella Buster! Hey, that sounds like it might make a neat song.

Muzzle Nuzzles, Koani

Motel Canines

IN MY LAST LETTER, I described the van and said I'd tell you about camping the next time. Before I do that, I've got a little story about the van. We were in San Diego, California, where we'd just done a bunch of programs. Bruce and Pat packed the van, preparing to travel north. Me, I travel light–I've got nothing to pack. So I waited in the van; that way I can save my place on the bus. Three guys–they must've been fourth or fifth graders–walked up to the van and pointed in at Koani's empty kennel while whispering and staring. Now remember, the kennel is made with steel and chain-link fencing, and it's big, because Koani is a big canine. Bruce eventually walked out with more things to pack. (Humans seem to need so much stuff to live.) He said "hi" to the kids.

One of the boys said, "What goes in that cage?"

"We travel with a wolf," said Bruce.

The boy elbowed the other boy in the ribs, " Seeee, I told you it ain't for no bunny!"

Nope, Koani sure ain't no bunny, and that's what makes traveling with her such a challenge. For instance, think about getting a motel room when there's a wolf in your entourage. Most of the time, we camp out or stay in somebody's back yard. But if we're traveling and it's stormy, cold, and snowy, Bruce and Pat bite the bullet and get a motel room. And that's fine by me; I don't see anything adventurous or romantic about sleeping out in below-zero temperatures with the snow blowing sideways.

Getting a motel room isn't as easy as you might think. In the first place, the motel has to be located on the outskirts of town so we have access to big fields, parks, or other open space, because we go on our wolf walks twice a day, morning and evening. Think about heading out on a wolf walk from a motel surrounded by stores, malls, and busy roads. Here's the other thing that adds an extra challenge to getting a room–and I know you'll have a hard time believing this, but it's true: some motels allow only one kind of animal in their rooms, and that's the human animal. They don't let dogs or cats or any other animals indoors.

While Pat and Bruce don't lie, full disclosure isn't one of their virtues. Here's what I mean: Pat walks into the motel office and inquires as to whether they allow pets or not. If they say "yes," she says, "That's good, we'll take a room–one down at the far end if you've got it, please." She doesn't mention that one of her "pets" is a mammalian velociraptor.

One time, the motel man said, "No, we don't allow pets in the rooms, but I think my friend does, and he runs a motel down the road." He called his friend and asked about pets. Now keep in mind that this guy never looked at or even asked about Koani and me. So, his friend said something we couldn't hear, and the motel man answered, "No, no, no, these aren't wolves, these are cute little pooches." He looked at Pat and Bruce with a smile and winked. They just smiled back.

We're getting ready for another road trip to do our California Program Tour. But Eliott Steele just showed up–he's the German shepherd from across the creek. He barks right in Koani's face and bites her on the rump. He's sooo immature. It's my duty to straighten him out. Hey, I gotta go. Seee ya!

 Love, Indy

The Ms. Chloe Dog Cook Blues

February 2, 1996

THIS IS MS. CHLOE DOG COOK. I suppose you know that I am Koani and Indy's best friend in the whole wide world. I'm sorry to say that my spirits are sinking dreadfully low this morning. You see, the whole gang just left again for a long trip filled with programs, talks, and countless adventures. Who knows how long they'll be gone?!? Does anyone ever stop to think about what I'm doing while they're off on all those wild adventures you've been reading about? I wait! That's right. I just sit and wait. And worry.

I'm a dog who prefers routines. After they've been in town for a day or so, I wake up bright and early ready for adventure. Keep in mind the early morning hours are hard on a Great Dane who usually sleeps until noon. Nevertheless, when Koani and Indy come to town, I run downstairs with youthful enthusiasm and start my window-guarding activities. I race from window to window, watching for the pack to round the corner. When I see them, I signal my human companion, Genny, and dash to the front door. As with all of my responsibilities, I take this job quite seriously.

But when my friends are off doing Wild Sentry programs, do you know what happens? I don't see them come around the corner. And they don't show up that evening or the next morning, either. The conclusion is obvious; they're gone again and maybe for good this time. The only thing left to do is to find my cedar-chip pad, hang my head, and sigh.

I'm sure you can feel my pain. But I haven't even told you the most distressing part! All of this despair and heartache is completely avoidable. I am more than willing to hop in the van and become a part of their traveling road show. And I would be good too. As some of you may recall, I was once a celebrity guest star for a Wild Sentry program. Everyone said I was certainly a sensation! And that was even before I started wearing my distinguished Harlequin Great Dane collar.

It just doesn't make sense to me. Their program is all about wolf education and teaching people the real story of the wolf. Well, Koani and I have been packmates for as long as I can remember. I'm sure I know just as much or more about wolf behavior as Pat, Bruce, and Indy. I could keep people entertained and informed for hours with stories about Koani. And of course, it's hard for people not to be attracted to my good looks and personality at the same time. The programs would all sell out.

By this point, you may be wondering what you can do to help me correct this injustice. I assure you, it is a worthy cause. I thought maybe if I wrote this letter, you would help me convince them to make a few important changes in their program. I really hope so, because I cry often and miss them deeply. I can pack lightly: just my cedar-chip pad, a change of collar, and some food. If you see them, please tell them to come back for me soon before I get too fat from eating all of the consolation cookies Genny offers. I implore you—get behind the movement, support something real for a change, and send me your suggestions for rallying cries!

Truthfully, Responsibly,
Full of Talent,
and Tired of Waiting
I remain, Respectfully Yours,
Ms. Chloe Dog Cook

Motel Wolf

February 9, 1996

We're traveling again! I don't know exactly where we're headed, but the farther we travel, the warmer and drier it gets. Last night it snowed, so all of us stayed in a house. Even though it was a huge house, we only got to see the inside of one room, with a little white room to the side. After I looked out the one and only window, I ran into the little white room, grabbed a smelly, plastic-wrapped thing, and rolled in it. [Editor's note: She's referring to a bar of soap.] But my enthusiasm waned quickly because I was tired from riding in the van all day. There was only one bed in the room, and Bruce and Pat had spread an old blanket on top (to make me feel at home, I guess). So I jumped on the bed, dug around in it to make a nest, and curled up for a nap. Every once in a while, Bruce or Pat or Indy tried to get on the bed with me. I curled my lips and growled. They backed off. After all, I took the bed first.

Finally, I got too hot, even though they had turned the heat off and opened the window (but not far enough for me to squeeze through). So I stretched out on the floor. Then Bruce and Pat and Indy all got on the bed, and none of them growled at each other. Pretty weird.

Sometime in the middle of the night, I heard a truck approach and saw its lights coming towards our window! SCARY! I jumped up and ran across the bed to get to the other side of the room. I heard Pat or Bruce go, "Ooooooomph!" Indy yipped when I stepped on his tail.

Fortunately, the truck stopped before it smashed through the wall, so we were okay.

The next morning, even before the sun rose, I woke everyone up to go for a walk. At home, sometimes they stay in bed and ignore me for an hour or more. But when we're in rooms like this, they always bolt out of bed right away! I'm not sure why, because I could entertain myself pretty well for hours–there are curtains to shred, table legs to chew on, chairs to scent mark, the insides of pillows to explore, toilets to stick my head into–the possibilities are endless.

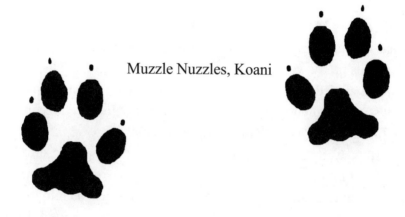

Muzzle Nuzzles, Koani

Stinky Tail

March 25, 1996

I'M BACK IN MONTANA! It's great. California's okay but it's too hot, it has too many cars, too many people, and too many malls, and the air smells pretty weird in a lot of places. Speaking of smells, guess what happened last night? Bruce and Pat walked down the road to visit some neighbors. Before they left, they put Indy in the pen with me (usually he's a couch potato in the evenings).

Anyway, as they walked away they told him to make sure I didn't get into trouble. YEAH SURE! That's like telling a four-year old human to guard the cookie jar. Indy always gets us into trouble, but he looks so innocent that I almost always get blamed. I bet some of you who have brothers and sisters know just what I'm talking about.

NOTHING ever happens in the pen–except when he's around. You'd think that sometime they'd figure it out. But humans aren't very smart. So anyway, after they left, Indy was moping around, acting like he'd been abandoned forever. He looked so depressed that he made me feel sad. I started howling so Bruce and Pat would know they should come find us. They didn't. Like I said, humans aren't very smart.

After a while, he realized no one was there to see his big sad eyes, so he started to snoop around the pen in search of bones and pieces of meat I'd stored away for a rainy day. There are a couple reasons that I have to keep an eye on him at times like that. The first reason is that I kind of enjoy watching the game, and the other is that I have

"Speaking of smells, guess what happened last night?"

to make sure he doesn't find my very best treasures. So I followed him around instead of curling up and going to sleep like I should have. And that's when we found it.

Actually, Indy and I have seen them before, but always with Pat and Bruce. When we see one, they yell and scream at Indy and drag me away, so we've never been able to get close. It's not very fair because this animal is only about the size of a cat and doesn't even have sense enough to run away from big, tough predators like me. Last night we found out why. Indy saw the catlike animal first and went bounding forward with me right after him. But the animal didn't even bare its wimpy little teeth at us. Instead it turned around, pointed its rear end at us, and flicked its tail up! Can you believe that? So, of course I figured, "Perfect."

I rushed forward to grab it before Indy could. Suddenly, my eyes stung. I coughed. I felt like throwing up. A terrible smell clouded the air. That was enough for me. I never really cared if it walked through my pen anyway. Indy barked at it for a while, but even he had sense enough to keep his distance.

We were pretty happy to see Pat and Bruce when they got home. But they didn't appear so happy to see us–or happy to smell us, anyway. We don't agree very often about what smells good or bad, but we did agree that this new scent smelled bad. But I'm a wolf, and we wolves really like to share a smell. Since there's no way to stop Indy and me from entering the living room pen, we both slept indoors last night. But right now, it smells so bad in the house, I think I'd better go outside.

Muzzle Nuzzles, Koani

Ticks and Scientific Research

April 1, 1996

BRUCE AND PAT TELL PEOPLE that I have an identity crisis. They say I don't really know who I am or what it is I want to do with my life. Sometimes I think they're a bit out of line speaking for me like that; but there's probably a tiny crumb of truth to the identity crisis thing. After all, I never knew my Dad. And the only thing I remember about Mom is her telling me, "Keep a positive attitude. I've got a feeling you're going to need it." Most of you know I landed in dog prison three times, and the last time I escaped doom by only a matter of minutes. So maybe I am a bit confused–but just a little and only once in a while.

I know one thing for sure. I'm the star of the Wild Sentry program. Isn't that enough? Well, isn't it?

Okay, sometimes even I think there's more to life than being a star. So when a new opportunity opened up to me last week, I figured I'd try it out. This opportunity I'm talking about was the chance to be a scientific research dog. The only thing is, now that I've actually been one, I don't think I want to do it again. In fact, I'm real certain about it–no more science for me. Here's why.

It all started with ticks. I met up with these particular yucky, icky, blood-sucking ticks when we were back East in New York. I'm talking about the New York countryside, not New York City. When most

123

people out West think of New York, they envision a BIG CITY, but most of the state of New York is forests and hills. Well, deer ticks jumped me in the wilds of New York. They hung from branches and bushes all over and everywhere. After a walk in the woods of Tarrytown (which is where Sleepy Hollow is located, which is where the Headless Horseman rides on Halloween Night, which is a whole 'nother story), Pat took sixty-three deer ticks out of my fur. Ticks are nauseating enough, but eastern deer ticks really make me gag because more than half of them carry Lyme disease, which can make dogs and people really sick if it isn't treated.

We have a friend in Montana named Tom who is a research scientist just like the ones you see in movies, except he doesn't laugh madly down in a dungeon or basement or castle full of glass tubes with bubbling chemicals and sparking bolts of electricity as he works to create monsters. No, Tom is a world expert on Lyme Disease. What he saw after looking at my blood under a microscope excited him, and he exclaimed, "Indy is full of antibodies fighting the Lyme disease spirochetes! I've never seen such a high level! He's a textbook case! It's fantastic! Can I have a tissue sample and more blood?" I certainly didn't like hearing that, but I felt better after he said, "Oh, by the way, there's nothing to worry about. Lyme disease is totally treatable. Indy can't pass it directly to anyone and, fortunately, our ticks in Montana don't carry Lyme disease."

Pat arranged a visit with Dr. Applebury, our official Wild Sentry vet. They put me on that slippery stainless steel table. Dr. Applebury placed a plastic muzzle hood over my mouth with a tube leading from it to a bottle of gas. He turned a valve, and I couldn't help but breathe the gas. I felt drowsy and that scared me. I started whimpering and whining. The last thing I saw was Dr. Applebury coming at me with a huge, sharp knife. Then I zoned out.

When I came to, the side of my head felt itchy. I scratched at it, and Pat got all excited and said, "Don't scratch your head. You've got stitches." And that's not all. In addition to thread in my head, I was missing a whole patch of hair and a chunk of skin. I'd been scalped! Pat tried to console me by saying that Tom needed the skin for a tissue sample, and it was all in the name of science, now that I was a real research dog.

Well, EXCUSE ME, but if being a research dog means getting gassed, scalped, cut, and stitched, then you can keep it. I'll stick with being a star. They're just lucky they didn't try that stunt with Koani or they'd be missing fingers. Maybe I'm too nice of a guy. Hey, I gotta go and see if my fur is growing back yet. Seee ya!

Love, Indy

The Truth about Montana's Last Wolf

April 20, 1996

I JUST RETURNED FROM Stanford, Montana. That's where, in 1930, a barbarian shot and killed the last wild Montana wolf. Being there felt a little scary, but everyone seemed to like me okay. After the program, we went to see the famous "White Wolf of Stanford." He's stuffed and stands inside a big glass case. Stuffing animals is another weird thing you humans do. I believe in eating what you kill, not stuffing it. The White Wolf stands there with a horrible, ferocious snarl permanently molded into his muzzle. Once in a great while I snarl like that, but it certainly isn't anything I do very often. I don't understand why humans stuffed him in such a pose. I guess they wanted him to appear mean so they'd feel good about having killed him. His tail is curled up like a sled dog's, which is so fake because wolves never curl their tails like silly dogs. Just shows you how much those people knew about us wolves, doesn't it?

The sign on the glass case said this wolf killed thousands of cattle during his eighteen-year "reign of terror" before some bovine-brain shot him. This sounded pretty fake to me. First of all, he couldn't have been eighteen years old. Wolves hardly ever get that old even in captivity, where we're fed food that doesn't kick and break bones and teeth. A wolf that hunts for a living would be considered really old if it reached the age of eleven. So he certainly couldn't have killed as many cows as people blamed him for killing. The sign also said he'd kill a cow, take a bite, and then move on and kill another cow. They made it sound as if there was something bad or wrong about that. Well, think about this: Imagine if people chased you and tried to shoot you or poison you. Do you think you'd sit around long enough to eat a whole cow? If you wanted to live very long, you wouldn't have time for that. People are so strange. You make wolves behave in ways we normally wouldn't, and then you hate us and tell awful stories about us for behaving that way.

So, all in all, I think humans made up most everything about the White Wolf of Stanford. But don't tell anyone I said that. You humans are pretty territorial about the stories you tell. And you know what else? I think you like monsters even if you have to create them in your imaginations. And if that's what you're inclined to do–well, I guess it's okay, just as long as you don't kill real animals because you've got an over-active imagination. Now the White Wolf, he could have told some stories about REAL monsters.

Muzzle Nuzzles, Koani

Birthdays and Full Moons

May 5, 1996

Guess what? I'm five years old today! All of us wolves have our birthdays in late April or early May, so you can sing the happy birthday song for all of us. When I was born, I weighed a pound and was smaller than my head is now! Of course, I don't remember that, but Bruce and Pat say it's true. I grew awfully fast that first year. At three months of age, I was still smaller than Indy, but not by much. By the age of six months, I weighed 75 pounds! Pat said I grew so fast that she worried I might get as big as a Tyrannosaurus Rex!

By the end of my first year, I'd grown so much, both physically and emotionally, that I was at the same stage of development as a 13-year-old human. Pretty good trick, huh? Six months later, at a year-and-a-half-old, I should've been able to get a driver's license. By the end of my second year, I was the equivalent of a 22-year-old human (except much smarter and a better hunter, of course). I felt kind of restless and pushy during that year. If I'd been free, I might have left my pack. Do you know any teenagers who act that way?

By three I was a fully grown adult, and now at five I'm middle-aged, like humans in their late-30s. It's a good age to be. I'm tough and physically fit. I know and am content with who I am. I'm

Howling together helps the group to bond and feel like a team.

big, I'm bad, I'm beautiful, and I don't let anyone shove me around (except Indy).

Last night, to celebrate my birthday, Pat took me and Indy for a walk under the full moon. It was BIG FUN. I don't see why we can't do it every night.

I've heard that lots of people think wolves howl at the moon. Well, that's not entirely correct. I'll tell you a few reasons that wolves howl. We howl to find other pack members if we get separated from them, the same way you'd whistle or shout if you got separated from the group you were hiking with. If wolves from another pack enter our territory, we howl and warn them to keep out–it's like shouting at them to get off our property. You humans do the same thing with fences and "No Trespassing" signs. We also howl before a hunt. When you don't have any tools or weapons, hunting is a very dangerous business. Howling together helps the group to bond and feel like a team, which is important if you're going to tackle a moose. Now here's where the moon enters the picture: A big moon gives off lots of light, which allows wolves to hunt during the night. But before we hunt, we howl. We're not howling at the moon; we're howling to form a team so we can go hunting by the light of the full moon.

Oh yeah, there's another reason that we wolves howl: just for the fun of it! You should try howling sometime–it feels good!

Muzzle Nuzzles, Koani

Fan Mail

May 9, 1996

Sᴜɴ ᴄᴇ ᴡᴇ ʀᴇᴛᴜʀɴᴇᴅ from central Montana, not much has happened. No big adventures, no narrow escapes—well, I did encounter the moose while on a walk with Uncle Gray. [Editor's note: Uncle Gray is the only person who's qualified to walk Koani without Bruce or Pat along. When Koani was young, Gray took the intrepid canine duo on many wolf walks. But life led him to Ontario and a wolf research project. Occasionally, he visits and takes Koani and Indy on walks.] Even though I got the moose to run after me, he stopped when he saw Koani and Gray, so it wasn't nearly as exciting as a couple of winters ago, when a moose tried to trample Koani, Bruce, and me.

Since I don't have any adventures to report, I'll tell you about some of the mail we got from students at the schools in central Montana where we did programs. Here's what Katrina Simpson wrote: "Koani and Indy were neat. I enjoyed seeing your program. I now can drive my annoying cousin crazy with your wolf howl."

Sounds like fun to me, even though I'm not one to howl much—in fact I don't howl at all. Koani is the howler.

Tyler Morris wrote, "Thanks a lot for bringing the wolf and dog. The wolf looked really cool and it's really big and has a very solid face. The wolf looked like he was going to attack at any time. Thank gosh he didn't." Of course, you all know that Koani is a she. I'm the he. Humans often think of wolves as being guys. Why do you think that is?

131

I bet you remember that wolf pups lick adult wolves on the muzzle to get them to regurgitate food for them. After wolves grow up, they still lick muzzles to show that they're friendly and want attention. Dogs, being related to wolves, lick the faces of their humans for the same reason. Levi Heller, who will probably grow up to be a scientist, wrote about an experiment he did with his dog. "I learned lots of stuff when you came. When I went home, I wanted to see if my dog licked me on the mouth. It did, but I didn't throw up."

My favorite letter came from Rex Reilly: "Thank you for bringing Koani and Indy. The dog was cooler, but the wolf was also cool. Indy was awesome."

Need I say more? Hey, I gotta go. Seee ya!

Love, Indy

Important Directions: Proper Methodology for Rolling in Poop

May 20, 1996

WHAT A GREAT WEEK! The main reason I say that is that the horses are back in the upper meadow where we walk almost every evening. You know what's great about horses, don't you? Horse POOP! L'Essence de Equs Eliminée is one of the cooler perfumes to wear–not the coolest, but Pat won't let me talk about the scent I love to roll in more than anything else. Recently it occurred to me that maybe the reason I never smell you humans wearing L'Essence de Equs Eliminée is that you don't know the best way to wear it or even how to put it on. Therefore, I'm going to give you detailed instructions so you can be as cool as I am. I've also noticed that dogs don't have the technique down as well as I do, so call your dog and maybe he or she can pick up some of the finer points of scent rolling. Listen carefully–you may even want to get paper and pencil and write this down so you don't forget.

    1. Find the right poop. It needs to be fresh, olive green in color, and moist. If it's still steaming, so much the better! Old, dried-up poop is NOT cool; it doesn't smell nice and fresh, and it lacks that "cling" quality. You don't want to go to all this trouble only to find that you have to repeat the process five minutes later.

133

2. Know where to wear it. It's best to apply most of the L'Essence de Equs Eliminée from chin to neck. A few dabs along your jaw and a streak or two down your back and rib cage are good, but it's your chin and neck that need the full treatment.

3. Approach the poop pile with all four feet on the ground.

4. Sniff the pile to check for freshness and consistency. If you're not sure, nibble and test.

5. Proper positioning is vitally important. If you've found the right stuff, let one of your front legs buckle. (I usually begin with my right, but that's a matter of personal preference.) At the same time, turn your head in the opposite direction so that your neck and shoulder are situated directly above the pile, and drop. **Important:** Don't allow your other front leg or back legs to collapse–yet.

6. Chin up! Turn so your chin now rests in the pile. Move your chin back and forth rapidly to make sure its well coated. Remember, this is fun. Wag your tail, half-close your eyes, and smile.

7. Attain maximum smear. Let your other front leg collapse, and with your head facing in the other direction, push yourself slowly forward with your back legs. Be sure to wriggle around as you perform this step.

8. Stand up and survey. You should now have a nice layer under your chin, some applied along your jaw, globs of it smudged down one side of your neck, and shoulder, and a streak smeared across your rib cage.

9. Repeat with the other side.

10. Go for a back smear. If there's enough left, lie down on top of the pile (which should be somewhat flattened by now), stick all four legs in the air and skootchy around to get a layer on your back. This is difficult and will require some practice. Don't worry about getting it just right the first time. Remember, this is supposed to be fun, so don't get all uptight. The most important thing is to enjoy yourself.

11. Shake it up, baby. Stand up, shake yourself to get rid of any excess, and ENJOY!

"Go for a back smear."

If done properly, not only will you have a nice, greenish tinge to your body, but you will smell WONDERFUL. When you know you smell wonderful, you not only feel more confident about yourself, but everyone you come in contact with will want to hover around and sniff you. We all know how important it is to be the center of attention.

I hope these directions are clear. I'm thinking maybe I should make a video that demonstrates the proper method for rolling in poop. Would you buy one?

Muzzle Nuzzles, Koani

A Full-Blown Body Whomper

June 24, 1996

I<small>T'S</small> 3:30 <small>A.M—AS IN, VERY EARLY MORNING,</small> way before the sun even thinks of rising–and we've just returned from an ADVENTURE. This was the kind of adventure that Pat and Bruce call a "full-blown body whomper." Participating in a full-blown body whomper means that you come home feeling like you've run a marathon on your knees, only to have a troop of hyperactive gorillas use you for a trampoline, followed by a herd of athletic elephants kicking you around like a soccer ball. In other words, I feel wicked stiff, exhausted, sore, and tired. I'm not going to crawl off this couch for a week. You might wonder, how can anyone feel so wiped out this early in the morning? Well, what started as a pleasant little outing yesterday morning turned into an epic forced march that lasted eighteen hours. We hiked at least twenty-five miles, which also included going up and down six thousand feet.

Here's what happened. We set out to climb Trapper Peak, a mountain that's more than ten thousand feet high. This should've been a delightful twelve-mile jaunt–had the humans known what they were up to. The climbing team consisted of me, Bruce, Carol Alette, Genny Cook, and Pat and Koani who were connected to each other with the leash. You might recall that Genny belongs to Ms. Chloe Dog Cook. Chloe, lucky for her, remained at home recovering from a foot injury. The ascent of Trapper went pretty smoothly. On the way up, a little snowstorm blew down on us, which is kind of novel for June. We held a council to decide whether or not to keep

137

going. Of course, I voted to carry on, as would any noble adventure dog. So upward we continued, over snow slopes and boulder fields to the summit. Up on top, Koani immediately fell asleep using a rock for a pillow. I'll admit I was too nervous to sleep–we were a long ways up! Some people might think that I'm scared of heights. DOUBT IT! What horrifies me are the depths. When you're on top of Trapper Peak peering over the sheer north face, you're not worried about what's above you–there's only sky up there–it's the thought of falling all the way down to the rocks below that makes me crawl on my belly.

Finally, we began our descent. Bruce, Genny, and Carol strapped skinny sticks to their feet and did what they called "telemark turns." Koani and I chased them. Pat, attached to Koani's leash, slid behind us on her bottom. It was so much fun that we did it again.

And that's where the fun ended.

Below there, we encountered sun-cupped snowfields. The best way to envision what it's like to walk on a sun-cupped snowfield is to imagine yourself the size of Barbie or Ken and having to hike for a couple miles down a slope of slushy egg cartons. But our real troubles began later, when the humans realized we'd traversed too far to the left. We traversed right and still we couldn't find our route back to the van. We sat down and held another council to decide which way to go next. Now, I'll have you know both Koani and I realized we should continue to the right. But did Pat, Bruce, Carol, and Genny listen to us? Nooo way! They turned left again. To make a long story short, we muddled our way through dense forests, fallen timber, clouds of mosquitoes, slippery bear grass, and wet, swampy muck, and finally the humans realized we were lost. Then it rained. Bruce and Pat won't admit to being lost; they say we were "displaced." Actually, being lost never bothered me because I was having a grand old time, but the humans sure looked woebegone about it. However, I do have to give them credit because no one ever whined, though every once in a while I did hear them say words that shouldn't be repeated.

Finally, with night just around the corner, we reached a road. Unfortunately, it was the wrong road. We followed that road to its end, where we were faced with two options: (1) continue down into a deep abyss, crash through a dismal, dark forest of dog-hair pine and slide alder, and climb up the other side of the drainage in hopes of finding the right road, or (2) follow the wrong road clear down to the bottom of Trapper Peak where, we hoped, we'd hook up with the road that led to the van (which would be two thousand feet and six miles back up the mountain). With darkness setting in, we headed down the road and followed it to the base of the mountain, reaching the bottom at ten o'clock at night. Bruce and Genny then dropped their packs and skis and started on a six-mile trudge up the right road, while Pat, Carol, Koani, and I stayed behind with the gear. As Bruce and Genny disappeared into the night, I heard Bruce say, "One good thing is that it can't get any darker."

Around 1:30 in the early, early morning, they returned in the van–and I'm glad because I really didn't want to walk the rest of the way back home. Twenty-five miles was enough for one day! So now it's 3:30 and we're finally home. Everyone is feeling thoroughly body whomped. I'm on the couch, almost asleep, and there's no way I'm getting up. Oh, what's that I see? Bruce is preparing dinner for Koani and me. Oh boy, here it comes. Hey, I gotta go. Seee ya!

Love, Indy

Koani's Version
of the
Trapper Peak Epic

July 1, 1996

I'M GOING TO TEACH YOU an important lesson today. There are
AT LEAST two sides to every story, and I'm the only one who tells
the right one. I heard Indy's letter to you about our adventure on
Trapper last week. It was all mixed up. He acted like he knew we
should keep going to the right, and he never even mentioned how
we got off course in the first place. I sometimes think he and
Bruce are in cahoots because here's what really happened.

The very beginning of the descent was BIG FUN; after that, the
journey down turned into a forced march. I have to admit, even I
wasn't paying much attention. Everyone chattered and followed our
leader, Bruce, like good little wolf puppies; all except Indy who was,
of course, way out in front acting like Daniel Boone. Pat and Bruce
never pay attention to his directions because he's known as the Boy
of Little Brains.

Eventually, I realized that we were going down the mountain the
wrong way! I suggested to Pat that we should veer to the right. (Since

140

I don't have vocal cords like you humans, the only way I can suggest a change of direction is by pulling the leash). But did Pat listen? Nooooo. She kept pulling me back to follow Bruce. I insisted though, and finally I got through to her. I heard her tell Bruce, "I think we're too far to the left, we better go right."

"Yessss!" I said. I rapidly pulled Pat to the right and a little uphill. I knew if we continued down, there was going to be trouble. But she kept fighting me and refusing to do anything more than traverse horizontally across the slope. Meanwhile, I had no control over Bruce, Indy, Genny, and Carol. Bruce led them to the right but still steadily downhill. Of course, Pat didn't want us to get too far away from them, so she kept tugging me downhill. I want you to know it's hard to pull a human uphill in thick brush when they're obstinately veering downhill. They've got gravity on their side, and they can grab tree trunks and branches with their hands.

Despite their best efforts to muddle things up, I eventually led us to within a couple hundred feet of the trail and relaxed. I'll know better next time; they all sat down, pulled out a piece of paper with lines on it, talked a while, and got up. And then what did we do? Did we walk over to the trail? Nooooo. We headed left! I gave up. There's no teaching these dumb animals anything, and on top of that, I was tired of dragging Pat along. Humans insist on thinking they know everything.

I don't know why I tried to lead them to the van anyway. I hate the van. Furthermore, we wolves are used to going without food for several days, and I always carry my sleeping bag with me. I figured I was outfitted better than anyone else. Indy was set up pretty good, too. However, he never thought about the fact that no one carried his dinner or mattress.

THE REST, AS THEY SAY, IS HISTORY. I ended up hiking twenty-five miles and spent sixteen hours with a human attached to me. That certainly deserves mention in the Guinness book of wolf records. Indy and I felt so sorry for Pat and Bruce the next day that we didn't insist

141

on a walk (they are getting kind of old and stiff, you know). Well to be truthful–and after all, this is the TRUE story–Indy and I didn't really want to go on a walk very bad either.

So just remember: Don't believe everything you hear or read, especially when Indy tells the story.

 Muzzle Nuzzles, Koani!

The Trapper Peak Epic: Yet Another Point of View

July 7, 1996

HI! REMEMBER ME? I'm Ms. Chloe Dog Cook. I'm Koani and Indy's best friend and, I might humbly add, the only reason that they and their humans haven't been lost—that is, until a couple weeks ago. As you know, I was not included in their BIG Trapper Peak Adventure. Genny says she didn't take me because I had a hurt toenail. Can you believe it? Because of a hurt toenail, I didn't get to go on a great expedition. They'll be telling stories around the campfire about it forever, and I won't have anything to add. It doesn't seem fair.

When Genny got home, all I had to do was give one sniff and I knew she'd snuck off to be with Indy and Koani. How do you think that made me feel? After all, they're my friends, not hers. She only gets included because of me, and yet she has the nerve to go off on an adventure without me.

Genny says she's really glad I wasn't along, especially in light of what happened; that it wouldn't have been good for my toenail to scramble around through the brush for sixteen hours. But you know what? If I'd been along, we wouldn't have spent sixteen hours crashing through brush, because we never would have gotten lost in the first place. Genny says I'm just being a cedar-chip pad critic, but really, I am the only one, as far as I can see, who has an iota of responsibility. I am, as you know, a Great Dane. We're known for being smart, loyal, brave, and, I might add, truthful and responsible. As evidence, I want you to think for a moment; can you think of one time that the Three Canidteers ever got lost when I was along?

In case you're having to think about this, the correct answer is "NO." That pretty well proves my point, doesn't it? Don't get me wrong–I like Indy, Koani, Pat, Bruce, Genny, and probably Carol, though I've never met her. But sometimes you've got to tell it like it is, and obviously that pack should never have been allowed to go off unaccompanied by a Great Dane.

At any rate, I'm sure they learned their lesson. I trust I will not be left home alone again. By the way, my toenail is just fine now, thank you very much.

Truthfully and Responsibly Yours,
Ms. Chloe Dog Cook

Freedom or Security?

July 14, 1996

I'M BORED! NO SKUNKS, NO PIT BULLS, no moose, no thin ice, NOTHING. No traveling in the van even. I'm just here in Hamilton, and there's nothing to do except argue with Indy about bones and catch mice while out on walks. Do you ever get bored? Probably not, I guess. Humans seem easily entertained. I've seen people sit for hours staring at paper or at a little window with shadows moving in it. Every once in a while, I find it entertaining to tear paper into tiny pieces. But to just sit and look at it? Too weird. As for watching the little window, I'm glad it keeps you entertained, but we wolves need more interesting things to do. I guess that means our brains must be superior to yours.

Not that wolves require something going on constantly. After all, we need to sleep and nap for about twenty hours each day. That's why when we're up, we're UP and we need things to do and places to go. No wonder you can sit and stare at windows and paper and stuff. If I only got eight hours of sleep a day, I'd be so tired I'd probably stare at things, too.

Pat and Bruce keep telling me I'm pretty lucky, that most wolves living with people never get to go for walks outside their pens. I can't even imagine how awful that would be. How would you like it if you were never allowed to go outside of your house? Maybe I am fortunate compared to some wolves. I do go for walks every day. Pat and Bruce take me and Indy out in the morning and in the evening; those are the

145

times when we wolves are most awake. [Editor's note: Actually, wolves are crepuscular animals, meaning they favor the periods of half-light that occur between night and day.]

Sometimes, though, I think there ought to be more to life. Everyone says that as a teacher, I'm doing good things for wolves. But I didn't ask to be a teacher–maybe I'd rather be living with other wolves and killing elk and having pups. On the other hand, according to Pat and Bruce, wolves in the wild only live to be seven or eight because they get arthritis and their teeth wear out. I'm almost five already. I'll live to be fourteen or fifteen with Pat and Bruce taking care of me. So maybe it's better to be a little bored sometimes. But then again, maybe it's better to have a shorter life and live more intensely. What do you think?

I know what I'm going to do. I'm going to make something happen. I'm going to rip up my blanket. That always gets me some attention. You ought to try it sometime.

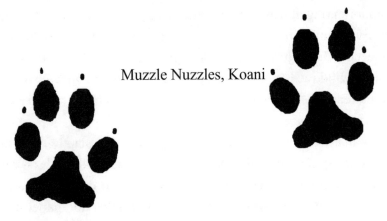

Muzzle Nuzzles, Koani

The Nightmare Child!

July 29, 1996

WE'RE HOME FOR ONE DAY, and then we have to do more programs. It's sort of a lull between storms. We just returned from Ketchum, Idaho, where we did a fun workshop for teachers.

You guys probably know that before teachers become teachers, they have to go to school and take special classes. If they get good grades and graduate from college, then they're qualified to give you homework. But I bet you didn't know that if teachers want to keep on teaching, they have to keep on taking classes every now and then. So, that's where I came in–I was a teacher for teachers. There's something kind of wicked fun about giving a teacher homework.

Here's something else that will probably surprise you: Some teachers are terrible students. You'd think that after all the time they spend teaching school, teachers would know how to be ideal students. To me, ideal students overflow with curiosity to learn all they can; they ask questions and want to talk about the subject. But some of the teachers I've seen make lousy students–not because they're loud, unruly, or rowdy, but because they just sit there drinking coffee and scribbling notes with absolutely no enthusiasm or smiles–like they're waiting for the dentist to drill a hole in their teeth. You ask a question in hopes of getting a discussion going and no one says a thing. It's like they're scared that if they give the wrong answer, Koani will bite them. Now, I'm happy to report that the teachers in Ketchum were ideal students. This particular group

This is Isaac Rockwell (not the Nightmare Child) hugging Indy.

of teachers was fun; they raised their hands, asked questions and discussed things, just like in school.

However, I didn't have much fun at the public program we presented that evening. Lots of kids worry at night about monsters under the bed. Me, I worry about encountering a NIGHTMARE CHILD in broad daylight. And I did in Ketchum. As you probably already know, when we do a program, Bruce and Pat tell stories and show slides for the first part and then they bring Koani and me in–they save the best for last. From what Bruce told me, a little four-year-old boy sat in his mother's lap making noise throughout the boring slide show part of the program. I guess the mother thought her toddler was cute, but no one else in the audience did. Every once in a while, when the kid made so much noise that Bruce or Pat couldn't concentrate, they'd stop and wait for the child to quiet down. Now you'd think that after stopping the program a few times, the mom would've gotten the hint and taken the unruly child out to the lobby. But noooo way.

Finally, Koani and I entered. Right off the bat, tension mounted when Koani spotted a ceiling fan. The fan wasn't even turning, but that didn't matter to Koani. Something about having those paddle-blades overhead makes her nervous. So, while she suspiciously eyed the ceiling, the NIGHTMARE CHILD decided he wanted to pet the wolf. Pat kept telling me to go visit the kid, but I didn't want anything to do with him. I love kids, all except that kind; they make me more nervous than ceiling fans do Koani. You never know what they'll do. Some of them yank my tail or ear or grab a handful of fur while emitting a gleeful scream.

Suddenly, he squirmed off his mother's lap and ran forward caterwauling like a mountain lion that had stepped on hot coals. He almost made it to the front of the room, but the mom snatched him by the seat of his pants and down they both went. He wiggled out of her clutches again and crawled towards Koani. Pat stepped between him and us, ready to tackle the kid. Fortunately, the mom grabbed his ankle, but when that happened, noise erupted from his mouth like

149

fiery lava spewing from an exploding volcano. He clawed at the rug and screamed and cried and carried on like it was the end of the world.

Meanwhile, Koani had decided that being caught between threatening ceiling fans and the NIGHTMARE CHILD was too much–she wanted out. I sat back and watched, as I couldn't do much else. It was quite a scene; Koani pulled, tugged, and whipped her head back and forth like a stubborn mule, while Bruce dug in his heels and held on for all he was worth. Pat became a defensive lineman and formed a human barrier between Koani and the NIGHTMARE CHILD.

Bruce eventually ushered me and Koani outside, and things must've settled down inside. But I'll tell you what–I think kids and parents like those two should be taken to obedience school, where they can learn how to behave around canines. Right now, Pat and Bruce are packing for some programs on the Blackfeet Indian Reservation. I hope there aren't any nightmare children up there.

I better save myself a place on the bus. Hey, I gotta go. Seee ya!

Love, Indy

Am I a Good Teacher or What?

August 5, 1996

W E JUST RETURNED FROM doing programs at a kids' wildlife camp on the Blackfeet Indian Reservation. We drove a long way, crossed the Continental Divide, and traveled up the east front of the Rockies. We camped out under the full moon, and first thing in the morning we watched the sun light up Chief Mountain. This place looks like good wolf country to me.

The kids really liked me, and I think I changed their minds about wolves. At the beginning of the program, Bruce and Pat asked them, "What words come to mind when you hear the word 'wolf'?" Here's a list of words that the Blackfeet kids associated with us wolves:

Frightening	Scary
Dog	Wild
Mean	Deadly
Moon	Howling

At the end of the program, after the kids had seen me, Pat and Bruce asked them the same question, "Now what words come to mind when you hear the word 'wolf'?" Here's the new list:

Shy	Howling
Big Paws	Alert
Furry	Young & Handsome
Scared (the wolf is scared of us)	

The kids camped in teepees, and I got to go in one. Pretty neat. Indy embarrassed us all when he lifted his leg on one of the teepee doors and scent-marked it. And people say I'm the uncivilized canine! I couldn't believe it.

So now we're back in Hamilton. Indy and I have lots to do, though. In fact, we're so busy that we've decided to take a break from writing letters until the middle of September. Here's what we're doing: We're working on a book titled *Tales of Two Canines*. The book will be composed of the best letters we've written so far! I know that most of the letters in the book will be mine because my letters are so much better than Indy's.

 Muzzle Nuzzles, Koani

I'm the Star!

May 18, 1998

GUESS WHAT? I'M BACK HOME and I don't have to go anywhere for a while. We'd no more than gotten back from California than we hopped back in the van and headed for Kalispell, Montana. And we were hardly home for a day when we hit the road again, crossed a tall mountain range [Editor's note: that was the Continental Divide], and headed for Lewistown, Montana.

But here's the big news; in between all that traveling, we had a movie crew here. I don't know if you know it, but I've been in lots of movies. In one movie I even played the part of a wild wolf being released into Idaho. I wish! Then again, maybe I only think I wish. Maybe it wouldn't be so great worrying about where my dinner was going to come from all the time.

[Editor's note: The reader might note that nearly two years have passed between this and the previous letter. There've been lots of letters written during that time and maybe one day they'll appear in another volume of Koani and Indy adventures. However, the intrepid canine duo insisted that we include the following two letters, in this book, so they could share their big news.]

But anyway, this was a different type of movie. Pat says it's an IMAX® movie, and if they use me, I'll be the only wolf in North America with ten-foot fangs. Wouldn't that be great? If Indy gets in the film, his teeth will only be five-feet long—still pretty good for a little guy like him. Don't tell him I said that, okay? Our teeth will be that big because IMAX movie screens are HUMONGOUS, or so Pat and Bruce say. It sounds good to me, so I'll pass it along. I do know the camera is gigantic and made a lot of noise, too.

Pat and Bruce were sure I'd be scared to death of the camera and wouldn't do anything but peer out from behind trees. But did I ever surprise them (as I know you know, it's good to keep your alphas a little confused about what you're going to do next—that way they don't start having unrealistic expectations). The crew filmed me coming down my tunnel to the house, walking across a log on the creek, and jumping off a cliff with Bruce—just like Indiana Jones. Indy (who's named after Indiana Jones chickened out and ran around). I did it all (sometimes more than once) just like a real actress.

Then they got the bright idea of filming me getting into the van to go do a program. I didn't like the getting-in-the-van part, so I didn't. After they quit filming, I got in. Like I said, if you do everything your agents tell you to do, it doesn't take long before they expect you to jump at their beck and call. Next we got filmed doing programs in schools.

Right now, I'm waiting for Bruce to get home from Missoula so he can take us for a walk. Pat's here but she's limping around and doesn't seem about to take us out. She says she strained a muscle in her leg. I'm wondering now that she's lame if it wouldn't be the right time to see if I could become the top wolf in the pack. That's how wolves get to be the leader or alpha wolf, you know. Out in the wild, as a lower-ranking wolf, I'd wait until a leader wolf showed some sign of weakness, and then I'd try to win a fight with it. If I did, I'd be leader and could expect the other wolves to show me respect.

For instance, since I rank lower than Pat and Bruce, I always put my ears and tail down when I greet them. That's one of the ways a wolf shows respect to a leader. If I got to be leader, I wonder how Pat would show respect. She doesn't have a tail and I've never seen her ears do anything but stick out. It's no wonder you humans are always getting into fights and big wars. You don't have any way to communicate!

Well, I better go. I promise I'll still remember you when I'm famous.

Muzzle Nuzzles, Koani

Indy and Koani

What a Big Head You Have, Koani

May 26, 1998

YOU PROBABLY READ KOANI'S LETTER about being in an IMAX film. And you probably detected that she thinks she's pretty important because she's a movie star. She heard about how an IMAX screen is eight stories high, which means that she'll be seventy feet tall with ten-foot canines. So all of this has gone to her head, and she thinks that she's pretty big stuff now.

The IMAX crew filmed her–actually, they filmed all of us, but Koani thinks they only came to film her–with a class of little kids at Corvallis School and at a program in a church in Hamilton. They arrived at Gopher Ranch and unloaded all kinds of movie stuff from two big trucks. They set up bright lights on long poles, which I thought was kind of odd seeing as the sun was still shining. They put up a big curtain in front of the lights, and I thought that was even stranger. Why go to the trouble of unpacking all those lights only to tack cloth in front of them? I heard one of them say that the curtain was quite thin and would diffuse the light–whatever that means.

Next, they set up the IMAX camera; it's the size of a cow calf and makes about as much noise as a tractor. They filmed Koani coming down her tunnel, and they filmed her entering her indoor enclosure. I have no idea why they found this interesting or why they thought anyone would want to watch this stuff on a big screen; it'd be about like filming you walking from your bedroom to the kitchen–big deal!

Then they loaded up all their movie-making stuff, set it up again, and filmed us–and I do mean US because they filmed all of us and not just Koani (which I think she tends to overlook) crossing a log over the raging stream. They filmed Koani getting a drink of water from the stream–wow, too exciting. They filmed Koani and Bruce sliding down a steep embankment, which I didn't do and not because I'm a chicken like Koani said but because I found the safe and sane way down. And finally, they wanted to film Koani getting into the van. The man in charge said, "What I'd like you to do is run out of the pen with Koani and have her jump into the van."

Bruce rolled his eyes, and I heard him mutter, "Oh sure, that'll happen about three minutes after Elvis gets elected president." Bruce and Koani ran out of the pen and right up to the van where Koani planted her feet and wouldn't get in. She told me later that she'd been too cooperative. Real movie stars are temperamental and every so often, in order to be appreciated, they need to throw a little fit.

Well, thank goodness they finally left because her head was getting so big that I don't think that she could've fit in the van if they'd stayed much longer. But ever since then, she's become a bit difficult to be around. For instance, she threw a little tantrum and knocked down our Montana trampoline. (In case you don't know what a Montana trampoline is, it's four piles of old tires stacked three high with a big, flat board on top.) Sometimes when we go out to get her for a walk, she won't get up, and she'll yawn as if to tell us that she's not sure if she should exert herself because it might muss her fur.

And from what I hear, the IMAX people are coming back to do more filming. That will just remind Koani of what a big movie star she thinks she is.

Oh sure, the IMAX movie is about wolves. But I'm sure to be in it too–I think. In fact, no one would even know about Koani if it weren't for me. Like I told you at the beginning of the book, I'm the star of the show, I'm the one who's cute, I'm the one everyone comes to see–aren't I?

Of course I am! I gotta go tell Koani about this. Seee ya!!!

Love, Indy

MORE ABOUT
WILD SENTRY

The Northern Rockies Ambassador Wolf Program

FOUNDED IN 1991, Wild Sentry blends science and the humanities to present an unbiased, educational, and entertaining program that challenges stereotypes and corrects misconceptions about wolves while examining cultural perceptions of wildness. If a picture is worth a thousand words, then the presence of a living, breathing animal is worth a thousand pictures. Few people have seen a wolf; nevertheless, they hold strong opinions based on campfire tales, legend, and folklore. In the wolf, some people see a hound of the devil, whereas others see a kindly shepherd that maintains the balance of nature. As an ambassador for her species, Koani dispels fears and misconceptions about an animal that stalks the human imagination.

At the turn of the century, wolves were exterminated from the Rocky Mountain region where, due to a depleted prey base, they turned to livestock. Today, things have changed–wolves have returned to a portion of their native haunts. However, their survival depends on people's attitudes towards them. Wolf recovery sparks controversy. Many opponents advocate the three S's: "Shoot, shovel, and shut up!" They display bumper stickers with slogans such as "Wolves: Nature's Criminals." On the other hand, naive proponents believe that wolves never kill healthy prey and never harm livestock.

The factual information presented by Wild Sentry provides a counterpoint to such sentiments and offers people a chance to see and understand the real wolf, not the creature colored by bias and fallacy that lurks in our imagination. While we can pass legislation aimed at protecting wildlife and wild lands, we can't legislate morality. Nothing truly changes without a change in attitude. Wild Sentry programs, a majority of which are presented in rural schools and communities within wolf recovery areas, are seen by more than 20,000 people annually.

**If you want to keep up with the
ongoing adventures of Koani and Indy,
become a member of the Wild Sentry pack.**

For a $25 or more tax-deductible donation, you get:

👍 A year's worth of Wild Sentry's newsletter

👍 A matted 5x7 color photograph of Koani

👍 Updates on where you can see Koani and Indy
and the Wild Sentry program

👍 The satisfaction of knowing your money supports
a grassroots organization that provides education
where it's most needed–rural schools and
communities located in the regions where wolves
are making a comeback.

To become a member of Wild Sentry, mail your check
or money order to (and don't forget to include your address):

Wild   Sentry
Box 172
Hamilton, MT 59840
email: <wildsent@bitterroot.net>
Web site: <http://www.bitterroot.net/wild/index.html>

Koani and Indy's Other Book
There's a Wolf in the Classroom!
by Bruce Weide and Patricia Tucker
Carolrhoda Books

THIS IS THE EXCITING STORY of a wolf, two people, and a dog who travel across America presenting the truth about wolves to students, ranchers, hunters, and other interested people. Discover what it's like to live with a wolf and to learn about the natural history and behavior of wild wolves.

Filled with full-color photographs, this firsthand account tells young readers how Bruce and Pat raised Koani from a pup and spent thousands of hours preparing her for classroom encounters. *There's a Wolf in the Classroom!* leads to an understanding of this mysterious, magnificent, and controversial animal.

Selected for Science Books and Films'
Annual Best Children's Science Book List

"What a cool book you published. When I looked up from the book, I thought my stuffed wolf was real for a moment. Your book made me feel like Koani was in the room, and that I've known about her all my life."
—Ellen Selm, Morgantown, North Carolina

"Your book is by far my most popular book of this year. It is almost always checked out."
—Candace Schmidt, Rappahannock Library, Fredericksburg, Virginia

There's a Wolf in the Classroom!
64 color photographs • 56 pages • $9^3/_8$ x $8^1/_8$
Reading level: Grades 3-5 (but the story will delight readers of all ages)
ISBN 0-87614-958-1 • Paperback $8.95

For a copy autographed by the entire Wild Sentry team, send a check or money order for $12 (the extra three bucks covers shipping and handling) to Wild Sentry, Wolf in the Classroom, Box 172, Hamilton, MT 59840

We encourage you to patronize your local bookstores. Most stores will order any title that they do not stock. You may also order directly from Mountain Press by mail, using the order form provided below or by calling our toll-free number and using your VISA or MASTERCARD. We will gladly send you a complete catalog upon request.

Some other Natural History titles of interest:

_____Beachcombing the Atlantic Coast $15.00

_____A Field Guide to Nearby Nature
     Fields and Woods of the Midwest & East Coast $15.00

_____Mammals of the Central Rockies $14.00

_____Mammals of the Northern Rockies $12.00

_____OWLS Whoo are they? $12.00

_____SPOTTED BEAR *A Rocky Mountain Folktale* $15.00

Please include $3.00 per order to cover shipping and handling.

Send the books marked above. I have enclosed $ _____

Name _____

Address _____

City _____ State _____ Zip _____

☐ Payment enclosed (check or money order in U.S. funds)

Bill my: ☐ VISA ☐ MasterCard Expiration Date: _____

Card No. _____

Signature _____

Mountain Press Publishing Company
P.O. Box 2399 • Missoula, MT 59806
Order Toll Free 1-800-234-5308
Have your Visa or MasterCard ready.